P9-DHZ-355

March of America Facsimile Series

Number 59

Travels in the Interior of America

John Bradbury

Travels in the Interior of America

by John Bradbury

ANN ARBOR
UNIVERSITY MICROFILMS, INC.
A Subsidiary of Xerox Corporation

56730

Foreword

The first edition of John Bradbury's *Travels in The Interior Of America, in the Years 1809, 1810, and 1811* appeared in Liverpool, 1817. The book, which achieved considerable popularity on both sides of the Atlantic, is significant for several reasons. It provided the public with one of the first detailed descriptions of the Missouri River Valley since the publication of the findings of the Lewis and Clark expedition of 1803-1806. It also supplied the public with information about the Ohio River Valley, into which poured a stream of emigrants from the eastern United States, from Great Britain, and from other countries. Because Bradbury wrote about Americans in a friendly, understanding manner, his book helped counteract some of the rather biting observations which other English travelers had made about the United States in the hostile climate of the War of 1812.

John Bradbury had been commissioned by the Botanical Society of Liverpool to investigate plant life in the United States. On Thomas Jefferson's advice, he determined to make St. Louis his base of operations. During the spring and summer of 1810 he undertook a number of short trips from St. Louis to collect plant specimens. In early 1811 he met Wilson P. Hunt, the leader of an expedition to the Pacific Coast for John Jacob Astor. Hunt invited Bradbury to come along. Bradbury accepted the invitation and accompanied the party some 1,800 miles up the Missouri River to the Arikara Indian villages. There he left Hunt's party and, with Ramsay Crooks, went another 200 miles up the Missouri to visit fur trading stations. Journeying back down the Missouri to St. Louis, Bradbury later descended the Mississippi to New Orleans, experiencing an earthquake en route. From New Orleans he sailed in January, 1812, for New York. Caught in America by the War of 1812, Bradbury remained four more years. After the cessation of hostilities he traveled through the western states and into the Illinois country before returning to England.

Bradbury devoted most of the space in his book to an account of his trip up the Missouri River. His journal reveals the keen enthusiasm of the dedicated scientist, ready to brave almost any hardship to obtain a desirable specimen. His descriptions of the country and his observations of the Indians reveal unusual discernment.

But Bradbury's remarks about the Ohio River Valley, though much briefer, also hold great interest. The cooperativeness of the westerners in organizing "frolics" and "bees" to help one another impressed him favorably. "In no part of the world is good neighbourship found in greater perfection than in the western territory, or in America generally," he wrote. The lack of class consciousness also won his applause. "That species of hauteur which one class of society in some countries show in their intercourse with the other, is here utterly unknown." The vast emigrations into the western United States demonstrated clearly, he thought, the superiority of that country. Nevertheless, the emigrant who settled in the West without careful forethought risked disappointment, he warned. It was because of superior planning and organization "that the Germans, Dutch, and Swiss succeed much better than those from any other country."

As proof of the genuineness of his admiration for western America, Bradbury returned after the publication of his book and settled in St. Louis. Reuben G. Thwaites gives a useful account of Bradbury and his journal in his edition of "Bradbury's Travels in the Interior of America, 1809-1811," in *Early Western Travels, 1748-1846* (Cleveland, 1904), V, 9-15.

Travels in the Interior of America

TRAVELS

IN

THE INTERIOR OF AMERICA,

IN THE

YEARS 1809, 1810, AND 1811;

INCLUDING

A DESCRIPTION OF UPPER LOUISIANA,

TOGETHER WITH

THE STATES OF OHIO, KENTUCKY, INDIANA, AND TENNESSEE,

WITH THE

ILLINOIS AND WESTERN TERRITORIES,

AND CONTAINING

Remarks and Observations

USEFUL TO

PERSONS EMIGRATING TO THOSE COUNTRIES.

———————◆———————

BY JOHN BRADBURY, F.L.S. LONDON,

Corresponding Member of the Liverpool Philosophical Society, and Honorary Member of the Literary and Philosophical Societies, New York, United States, America.

LIVERPOOL:

PRINTED FOR THE AUTHOR,
By Smith and Galway,
AND PUBLISHED BY SHERWOOD, NEELY, AND JONES, LONDON.

1817.

TO HIS EXCELLENCY

DE WITT CLINTON,

GOVERNOR OF THE STATE OF NEW YORK,

PRESIDENT OF THE LITERARY AND PHILOSOPHICAL
SOCIETY,

CITY OF NEW YORK, &c. &c.

THIS WORK

IS RESPECTFULLY INSCRIBED BY

THE AUTHOR.

PREFACE.

WHEN I undertook to travel in Louisiana, it was intended that I should make New Orleans my principal place of
residence, and also the place of deposit for the result of
my researches. This intention I made known to Mr.
Jefferson, during my stay at Monticello, when he immediately pointed out the want of judgment in forming that
arrangement, as the whole of the country round New
Orleans is alluvial soil, and therefore ill suited to such
productions as were the objects of my pursuit. In consequence of his representations, I changed my intentions,
and proceeded to St. Louis, one thousand four hundred
miles above Orleans by the course of the Mississippi,
where I employed myself, during the winter of 1810, in
making such preparations as I deemed necessary for the
preservation of what might be collected during the ensu-

ing summer. In my subsequent journey up the Missouri, although every facility was afforded me that the nature of the expedition would allow, yet the necessity of conforming to the rules laid down to secure the safety of the party during the voyage, added to the known or supposed proximity of the hostile Indians, during a considerable part of our route, caused me to lose a great many opportunities, which, had my exertions been free, I should not have done. Besides these impediments, I lost the opportunity of collecting a great number of new plants on my return, through the breach of faith towards me by Mr. Lisa, who agreed that his boats should land me at different places; which promise he neither did, nor intended to perform. For these reasons, I am persuaded that much yet remains to be done in that interesting country. When the whole of my collection was embarked on the Missouri, at the Aricara nation, it was extensive; but being then two thousand nine hundred miles from New Orleans, the losses by the way, and during my subsequent sickness at St. Louis, greatly diminished it. Immediately after my return to the United States, and before I could make any arrangement, either for my return to England, or for the publication of the plants I collected, the war broke out with this country :—I waited for its termination, and made some arrangements which caused a necessity for my stay some time longer.

I have made the above statement, because I think that whoever undertakes a mission of the nature which I did, where the duty is to be performed in a wilderness, ought to give an account how he performed it, even in his own defence; as it often happens that men are found, who, from interested or malignant motives, will vilify his character. I had intended that this should have been accompanied by a description of the objects collected, that had not been before discovered; but on my return to England, I found that my design was frustrated, by my collection having been submitted to the inspection of a person of the name of Pursh, who has published the most interesting of my plants in an appendix to the *Flora Americæ Septentrionalis.*

As my chief object has been to convey information and to write the truth, I have not been particular in the choice of words: if, therefore, the style meets with criticism, I shall neither be surprised nor disappointed. A catalogue of some of the more rare plants in the neighbourhood of St. Louis, and on the Missouri, is added, together with their habitats. To many it will be of no value; but as it may be of some use to naturalists who may visit those parts hereafter, I have thought proper to insert it. In what relates to the country west of the Alleghanies, I have been brief, because a more dilated account would have swelled the work much beyond the limits I had prescribed to myself. A second visit to those parts, in which my movements shall be less circumscribed, may enable me to give a more finished picture. In what has been said on those countries, I disclaim any design to encourage emigration; and may be credited in the assertion, because I can have no possible interest in promoting it. I have told the truth, and I can see no reason why it should have been suppressed.

Liverpool, August 1, 1817.

CONTENTS.

	Page
Arrival at St. Louis, ...	9
Departure up the Missouri, ...	11
Canadian Boatmen, ...	12
Arrival at Bon Homme Island,........................	14
Introduction to Daniel Boond, ...	16
Colter's interesting escape from the Blackfoot Indians, ...	17
Indian war parties, ...	23
Manitou rocks described, ...	24
Boond's Lick settlement, ...	25
The skunk, ...	27
Arrival at a village near Fort Orleans,.................	31
First appearance of sand-stone and iron ore, ...	32
Increase of bees, ...	33
Arrival at Fort Osage, ...	36
Description of an Osage village, and the manners of the inhabitants, ...	37
Wood pigeons described, ...	44
Coal discovered in the bluffs, ...	48
La Platte Rivière, ...	ib.
Indications of Indian war parties,.....................	ib.
Description of the lake and hills near Papillon creek, ...	49
Departure overland for the Ottoes, ...	53

b

Page

Description of the Otto village, ... 56
Thunder storm near Blackbird Creek,.................. 61
Blackbird's monument,.............................. 63
Account of Blackbird, *(note)* .... ib.
Maha village,.. 65
Introduction to the Big Elk and the White Cow, ... 68
The author meets with three Poncar Indians,............ 74
Iron ore in the bluffs, ... 80
A large Indian war party attempt to oppose the progress } 84
    of the boats, ... }
Smoking the calumet, ... 87
Character of the Sioux Indians, ... 89
The boats meet another party of Indians, ... 93
Mr. Lisa's boats come up, ... 97
Herds of buffaloes,.................................. 106
Indian hunting, ... ib.
Some account of the beaver,.......................... 107
Arrival at the Aricara town, ... 110
Account of the Indian language, ... 111
Indian council, ... 112
Medicine man, ... 116
The Aricaras prepare to defend themselves against the Sioux, 120
Journey overland to the Missouri Fur Company's Fort,.... 127
Cannon-ball river, ... 131
Arrival at the Mandan town, ... 137
Journey continued, ... 138
Arrival at the Fort, ... 139
Dance of the squaws, ... 146
Indian depository of the dead, ... 147
Instance of cruelty in an Indian chief,.................. 148
Excursion to the Mandan village,...................... 150
The author's rencontre with an Indian, ... 154
Return to the Aricara town,.......................... 156
Return of an Indian war party, ... 157

Page

Indian mode of hunting buffaloes, ... 163
Customs of the Aricara Indians, ... 165
Departure for St. Louis, ... 174
Tremendous thunder storm, ... 179
Battle of buffaloes,................................. 182
Arrival at Fort Osage, ... 184
Account of the Grand Saline, on the Arkansas river,...... 185
Arrival at St. Louis, ... 188
Departure for New Orleans, ... 193
Planters and Sawyers in the Mississippi,................ 194
Dangerous interview with Chickasaws, ... 196
Earthquake at the Devil's Channel,................... 199
Arrival at Natchez, ... 208
———— New Orleans, ... 209
Vocabulary of the Osage language, ... 213
Oration of the Big Elk, ... 220
Narrative of a journey from the Aricara nation to the Pacific Ocean, ... 222
MISSOURI TERRITORY, or the country of Upper Louisiana, 234
Its vast extent, ... 235
Cheap purchase of, ... 236
Immense salt deposit in Upper Louisiana, ... 242
Saltpetre generated in caves, ... 248
Lead Mines, ... 250
State of agriculture, ... 263
Cultivation of cotton, and a description of the saw gin,.... 269
Rapacity of the Spanish governors,................... 276
OHIO STATE,....................................... 279
Extent of land that furnishes water to the Ohio river, ... 282
Abundance of coal, ... 283
Salt, ... 284
Beauty of the native woods, ... 289
Price of land, and amount of land tax, ... 292
Trades and professions, and price of labour, ... 296

                                                                    Page
Constitution of the state of Ohio,...................... 300
Manners and hospitality of the Americans,.............. 304
Advantages of settling on the prairies,.................. 308
Remarks and observations useful to emigrants, ... 310
Catalogue of rare plants, ... 335
Letters on animalcula infusoria and on the physiology of⎫
    plants, ...⎭ 339

A JOURNAL, &c.

On the 31st December, 1809, I arrived at St. Louis, in Upper Louisiana; intending to make that town or neighbourhood my principal place of residence, whilst employed in exploring the interior of Upper Louisiana and the Illinois Territory, for the purpose of discovering and collecting subjects in natural history, either new or valuable. During the ensuing spring and summer, I made frequent excursions alone into the wilderness, but not farther than eighty or a hundred miles into the interior. In the autumn of 1810 I dispatched for Orleans, in seven packages, the result of my researches; but had the mortification soon after, to hear that the boat containing my collection had been driven ashore and damaged, on an island near St. Genevive, sixty miles below St. Louis. As soon as I received this information I went thither, but learned that the boat had been repaired, and had proceeded on her voyage. On my return to St. Louis, I was informed that a party of men had arrived from Canada, with an intention to ascend the Missouri, on their way to the Pacific Ocean, by the same route that Lewis and Clarke had followed, by descending the Columbia River. I soon became acquainted with the principals of this party, in whom the manners and accomplishments of gentlemen were united with the hardihood and capability of suffering, necessary to the backwoodsman. As they were apprized of the nature and object of my mission, Mr. Wilson P. Hunt, the leader of the party, in a very friendly and pressing manner, invited me to accompany them up the River Missouri, as far as might be agreeable to my views. I had intended to remove from St. Louis to Ozark, (or more properly Aux-arcs) on the Arkansas, and to spend the remaining summer on that river; but considering this opportunity for exploring the Missouri too valuable to be lost, I gladly accepted the invitation, to which an acquaintance with Messrs. Ramsey Crooks and Donald M'Kenzie, also principals of the party, was no small inducement. As it would not be practicable to ascend the Missouri until the breaking up of the ice in spring, Mr. Hunt concluded, that to avoid the expense of supporting his party at St. Louis, it would be better to station them during the winter on some part of the Missouri, at a con-

siderable distance above its mouth, as, at any point
on that river above the settlements, five or six hunters can easily provide for forty or fifty men. The
party therefore quitted St. Louis, and proceeded to
the mouth of the Naduet, which falls into the Missouri 450 miles from the Mississippi. In the beginning of March Mr. Hunt returned to St. Louis in
a boat with ten oars, and on the morning of the
12th, having completed his arrangements, he again
embarked for the Missouri. As the post was expected to arrive the morning following, I put my
trunks on board the boat, and determined to wait
until that time, and meet the party at St. Charles.
I must here observe, that the post to St. Louis is
dispatched from Louisville, in Kentucky, a distance of more than 300 miles, through a wilderness,
and from various causes is often retarded for several weeks, as had been the case at that period. In
the evening I was informed by a gentleman in St.
Louis, that a writ for debt had been taken out a-
gainst Dorion, (whom Mr. Hunt had engaged as
interpreter) by a person whose object was to defeat
the intentions of the voyage. I knew the detention
of Dorion would be of serious consequence to the
party, I therefore left St. Louis at two o'clock the
following morning, in company with a young Eng-
lishman of the name of Nuttall, determined to meet
the boat previous to its arrival at St. Charles, which
I effected; and Dorion was sent into the woods,

his squaw accompanying him. We arrived at St. Charles about noon, and soon after Mr. Samuel Bridge, a gentleman from Manchester, then living at St. Louis, arrived also, with letters for me from Europe, the post having come in as was expected. We slept on board the boat, and in the morning of the 14th took our departure from St. Charles, the Canadians measuring the strokes of their oars by songs, which were generally responsive betwixt the oarsman at the bow and those at the stern : sometimes the steersman sung, and was chorused by the men.* We soon met with Dorion, but without his squaw, whom it was intended should

---

* A few verses of one of their most favourite songs is annexed ; and to show its frivolity to those unacquainted with the language, an imitation in English is added.

I.

Derriere chèz nous, ilyă un etang,
    Ye, ye ment.
Trois canards s'en vont baignans,
Tous du lóng de la rivière,
Legérement ma bergère,
    Legèrement ye ment.

II.

Trois canards s'en vont baignans,
    Ye, ye ment.
Le fils du roi s'en va chassant,
Tous du lông de la rivière,
Legèrement ma bergère,
    Legèrement, ye ment.

accompany us. They had quarrelled, and he had beaten her, in consequence of which she ran away

---

III.

Le fils du roi s'en va chassant,
 Ye, ye ment.
Avec son grand fusil d'argent,
Tous du lông de la rivière,
Legèrement ma bergère,
 Legèrement, ye ment.—&c. &c.

I.

Behind our house there is a pond,
 Fal lal de ra.
There came three ducks to swim thereon;
All along the river clear,
Lightly my shepherdess dear,
 Lightly, fal de ra.

II.

There came three ducks to swim thereon,
 Fal lal de ra.
The prince to chase them he did run
All along the river clear,
Lightly my shepherdess dear,
 Lightly, fal de ra.

III.

The prince to chase them he did run,
 Fal lal de ra.
And he had his great silver gun,
All along the river clear,
Lightly my shepherdess dear,
 Lightly, fal de ra.—&c. &c.

from him into the woods, with a child in her arms, and a large bundle on her back. A Canadian of the name of St. Paul was sent in search of her. The day was very rainy, and we proceeded only nine miles, to Bon Homme Island, where we encamped, and St. Paul arrived, but without the squaw. I observed in the broken banks of this island a number of tuberous roots, which the Canadians call *pommes de terrè*. They are eaten by them, and also by the Indians, and have much the consistence and taste of the Jerusalem artichoke: they are the roots of *Glycine apios*.

15th.—About two hours before day we were hailed from the shore by Dorion's squaw, who had been rambling all night in search of us. She was informed that we would cross over to her at day break, which we did, and took her on board. I walked the most part of this day on the north side of the river, which is partly bounded by rocks of secondary limestone, at the foot of which I observed chrystals of quartz and calcareous spar, or carbonate of lime. We encamped opposite the remains of the village of St. Andrew, which is now abandoned.

16th.—We this day passed the Tavern Rocks, so called from a large cave therein, level with the surface of the river. These rocks are nearly three hundred feet high, and are of the same nature as those we passed yesterday, but more abundantly filled with organic remains, consisting of *anomiæ* and *entrochii.* On the islands which we passed there is abundance of *Equisetum hyemale,* called by the settlers *rushes,* by whom this plant is held in high estimation, on account of its affording winter food for their cattle. On the first settlement of Kentucky, the borders of the rivers were found to be thickly set with cane, *Arundinacea macrocarpon* of Michaux, and it was one of the strongest inducements with the first settlers to fix on a spot if cane was abundant. On the Missouri the rushes are equally valuable, affording to the first settler winter food for his cattle for several years, after which they perish, being destroyed if fed on during the winter. We this night arrived at Point L'Abaddie, where we encamped.

17th.—Early this morning I walked along the river, and was much struck with the vast size to which the cotton wood tree* grows. Many of those which I observed this day exceeded seven feet in diameter, and continued with a thickness very little diminished to the height of 80 or 90 feet, where the limbs commenced. After breakfast we

---

* Populus angulosa of Michaux, called by the French Liard.

crossed to the north side of the river, and in the afternoon landed at a French village named Cha- rette. In the woods surrounding this place I ob- served a striking instance of the indolence of the inhabitants. The rushes in the neighbourhood had been already destroyed by the cattle, and from the neglect of the owners to provide winter food for their horses, they had been reduced to the neces- sity of gnawing the bark off the trees, some hun- dreds of which were stripped as far as these animals could reach. The cotton wood, elm, mulberry, and nettle trees* suffered the most. On leaving Charette, Mr. Hunt pointed out to me an old man standing on the bank, who he informed me was Daniel Boond, the discoverer of Kentucky. As I had a letter of introduction to him, from his ne- phew Colonel Grant, I went ashore to speak to him, and requested that the boat might go on, as I intended to walk until evening. I remained for some time in conversation with him. He informed me that he was eighty-four years of age; that he had spent a considerable portion of his time alone in the back woods, and had lately returned from his spring hunt, with nearly sixty beaver skins. On proceeding through the woods I came to the river Charette, which falls into the Missouri about a mile above the village, and was now much swelled by

---

* Celtis crassifolia.

the late rains. As the boat had disappeared behind an island, and was at too great a distance to
be hailed, I got across by swimming, having tied
my clothes together, and inclosed them in my deer
skin hunting coat, which I pushed before me. I
overtook the boat in about three hours, and we encamped at the mouth of a creek called Boeuf, near
the house of one Sullens. I enquired of Sullens
for John Colter, one of Lewis and Clark's party,
whom General Clark had mentioned to me as being able to point out the place on the Missouri
where the skeleton of a fish, above forty feet long,
had been found. Sullens informed me that Colter
lived about a mile from us, and sent his son to inform him of our arrival; but we did not see him
that evening.

18th.—At day-break Sullens came to our camp,
and informed us that Colter* would be with us in a

---

* This man came to St. Louis in May, 1810, in a small
canoe, from the head waters of the Missouri, a distance of three
thousand miles, which he traversed in thirty days; I saw him on
his arrival, and received from him an account of his adventures
after he had separated from Lewis and Clarke's party : one of
these, from its singularity, I shall relate. On the arrival of the
party on the head waters of the Missouri, Colter, observing an
appearance of abundance of beaver being there, he got permission to remain and hunt for some time, which he did in company
with a man of the name of Dixon, who had traversed the immense tract of country from St. Louis to the head waters of the

few minutes. Soon after he arrived, and accompanied us for some miles, but could not give me

---

Missouri alone. Soon after he separated from Dixon, and *trapped* in company with a hunter named Potts; and aware of the hostility of the Blackfeet Indians, one of whom had been killed by Lewis, they set their traps at night, and took them up early in the morning, remaining concealed during the day. They were examining their traps early one morning, in a creek about six miles from that branch of the Missouri called Jefferson's Fork, and were ascending in a canoe, when they suddenly heard a great noise, resembling the trampling of animals; but they could not ascertain the fact, as the high perpendicular banks on each side of the river impeded their view. Colter immediately pronounced it to be occasioned by Indians, and advised an instant retreat, but was accused of cowardice by Potts, who insisted that the noise was caused by buffalo, and they proceeded on. In a few minutes afterwards their doubts were removed, by a party of Indians making their appearance on both sides of the creek, to the amount of five or six hundred, who beckoned them to come ashore. As retreat was now impossible, Colter turned the head of the canoe to the shore; and at the moment of its touching, an Indian seized the rifle belonging to Potts; but Colter, who is a remarkably strong man, immediately retook it, and handed it to Potts, who remained in the canoe, and on receiving it pushed off into the river. He had scarcely quitted the shore when an arrow was shot at him, and he cried out, " *Colter, I am wounded.*" Colter remonstrated with him on the folly of attempting to escape, and urged him to come ashore. Instead of complying, he instantly levelled his rifle at an Indian, and shot him dead on the spot. This conduct, situated as he was, may appear to have been an act of madness; but it was doubtless the effect of sudden, but sound reasoning; for if taken alive, he must have expected to be tortured to death, according to their custom. He was instantly pierced with arrows so numerous, that, to use the

the information I wished for. He seemed to have a strong inclination to accompany the expedition;

---

language of Colter, " *he was made a riddle of.*" They now seized Colter, stripped him entirely naked, and began to consult on the manner in which he should be put to death. They were first inclined to set him up as a mark to shoot at; but the chief interfered, and seizing him by the shoulder, asked him if he could run fast ? Colter, who had been some time amongst the Kee-kat-sa, or Crow Indians, had in a considerable degree acquired the Blackfoot language, and was also well acquainted with Indian customs, he knew that he had now to run for his life, with the dreadful odds of five or six hundred against him, and those armed Indians; therefore cunningly replied that he was a very bad runner, although he was considered by the hunters as remarkably swift. The chief now commanded the party to remain stationary, and led Colter out on the prairie three or four hundred yards, and released him, bidding him *to save himself if he could.* At that instant the horrid war whoop sounded in the ears of poor Colter, who, urged with the hope of preserving life, ran with a speed at which he was himself surprised. He proceeded towards the Jefferson Fork, having to traverse a plain six miles in breadth, abounding with the prickly pear, on which he was every instant treading with his naked feet. He ran nearly half way across the plain before he ventured to look over his shoulder, when he perceived that the Indians were very much scattered, and that he had gained ground to a considerable distance from the main body ; but one Indian, who carried a spear, was much before all the rest, and not more than a hundred yards from him. A faint gleam of hope now cheered the heart of Colter; he derived confidence from the belief that escape was within the bounds of possibility, but that confidence was nearly being fatal to him, for he exerted himself to such a degree, that the blood gushed from his nostrils, and soon almost covered the fore part of his body. He had now arrived within

but having been lately married, he reluctantly took
leave of us. I walked this day along the bluffs,

---

a mile of the river, when he distinctly heard the appalling sound
of footsteps behind him, and every instant expected to feel the
spear of his pursuer. Again he turned his head, and saw the
savage not twenty yards from him. Determined if possible to
avoid the expected blow, he suddenly stopped, turned round,
and spread out his arms. The Indian, surprised by the sudden-
ness of the action, and perhaps at the bloody appearance of
Colter, also attempted to stop, but exhausted with running, he
fell whilst endeavouring to throw his spear, which stuck in the
ground, and broke in his hand. Colter instantly snatched up
the pointed part, with which he pinned him to the earth, and
then continued his flight. The foremost of the Indians, on arriving at the place, stopped till others came up to join them,
when they set up a hideous yell. Every moment of this time
was improved by Colter, who, although fainting and exhausted,
succeeded in gaining the skirting of the cotton wood trees, on
the borders of the fork, through which he ran, and plunged
into the river. Fortunately for him, a little below this place
there was an island, against the upper point of which a raft of
drift timber had lodged, he dived under the raft, and after several efforts, got his head above water amongst the trunks of
trees, covered over with smaller wood to the depth of several
feet. Scarcely had he secured himself, when the Indians arrived on the river, screeching and yelling, as Colter expressed
it, " like so many devils." They were frequently on the raft
during the day, and were seen through the chinks by Colter,
who was congratulating himself on his escape, until the idea
arose that they might set the raft on fire. In horrible suspense
he remained until night, when hearing no more of the Indians,
he dived from under the raft, and swam silently down the river
to a considerable distance, when he landed, and travelled all
night. Although happy in having escaped from the Indians,

which were beautifully adorned with *Anemone hepatica.* We encamped near the lower end of Lutre (Otter) Island.

The 19th commenced and continued rainy. When we had passed the lower settlements, we began to see the river and its borders in a state of nature. The rushes *(Equicetum hyemale)* were so thick and tall, that it was both painful and difficult to walk along, even at a very slow pace.

20th.—The river on the south side, during this day's travel, is mostly bounded by bluffs, or rocks, of whitish limestone ; their appearance is very picturesque ; the tops are crowned with cedar, and the ledges and chinks are adorned with *Mespilus Canadensis,* now in flower. We encamped this night seven miles above the mouth of Gasconade river.

21st.—The rain had been almost incessant since

---

his situation was still dreadful : he was completely naked, under a burning sun : the soles of his feet were entirely filled with the thorns of the prickly pear ; he was hungry, and had no means of killing game, although he saw abundance around him, and was at least seven days journey from Lisa's Fort, on the Bighorn branch of the Roche Jaune river. These were circumstances under which almost any man but an American hunter would have despaired. He arrived at the fort in seven days, having subsisted on a root much esteemed by the Indians of the Missouri, now known by naturalists as *Psoralea esculenta.*

our departure from St. Charles, but had now ceased.
I went ashore, after breakfast, intending to walk along
the bluffs, and was followed by Mr. Nuttall. We
observed that the boat immediately passed over to
the other side of the river, on account of its being
more easy to ascend; as this sometimes happened
several times in a day, we felt no concern about
it, but proceeded on our researches. In the forenoon we came to a creek or river, much swelled
by the late rains; I was now surprised to find that
Mr. Nuttall could not swim : as we had no tomahawk, nor any means of constructing a raft, and
were certain that the boat was before us, we looked
for no alternative but to cross the creek by fording
it. We therefore continued to ascend, and in about
half an hour arrived at a place where a tree had
fallen in on the opposite side of the river, which
reached about half way across it. I stripped, and
attempted to wade to it, but found it impracticable.
I then offered to take Nuttall on my back, and swim
over with him ; but he declined, and we continued
our route. About a league further up, we found a
raft of drift-wood, which had been stopped by a
large tree that had fallen into the river; this we
crossed, and with some difficulty overtook the boat·
We arrived at a French village, called Cote sans
Dessein, about two miles below the mouth of
Osage river. After we had formed our camp, the
interpreter went into the village where he had some

acquaintance. On his return, he informed us that there was a war party of Indians in the neighbourhood, consisting of the Ayauwais, Potowatomies, Sioux, and Saukee nations, amounting to nearly three hundred warriors. He had learned, that this party were going against the Osages; but having discovered that there was an Osage boy in the village, they were waiting in order to catch and scalp him. He also informed us, that we might expect to fall in with other war parties crossing the Missouri higher up. This was unpleasant news to us, as it is always desirable that white men should avoid meeting with Indian war parties: for if they are going to war, they are generally associated in larger parties than can subsist by hunting, from which they refrain, to prevent being discovered by their enemies, wherefore they are almost certain to levy contributions of provisions or ammunition on all they meet. When they return from war, the danger is still greater; for, if successful, they often commit wanton ravages; and if unsuccessful, the shame of returning to their nation without having performed any achievement, often induces them to attack those whom they would, in other circumstances, have peaceably passed. As we were sixteen men, well armed, we were determined to resist any act of aggression, in case of a rencontre with them.

22nd, 23rd, and 24th.—Almost incessant rain ; our bread was now becoming very mouldy, not having been properly baked. Mr. Hunt anxiously waited for a fine day, to dry it, together with the rest of the baggage.

25th.—Met a boat with sixteen oars coming from Fort Osage to St. Louis, for supplies : news had arrived at the fort, that the Great Osages had lately killed an American at their village.

26th.—It rained nearly the whole of this day ; the flats near the river still continue to be so thickly covered with rushes, that it is next to impossible to travel over them.

27th.—The north bank of the river now assumes a most interesting appearance ; it consists of a range of rocks, nearly perpendicular, from 150 to 300 feet high ; they are composed of a very white limestone, and their summits are covered to the edge with cedar. The length of this range is about six miles, and at the upper end they assume a semicircular form. These are called the Manitou Rocks, a name given to them by the Indians, who often apply this term *Manitou* to uncommon or singular productions of nature which they highly venerate. On or near these Manitous, they chiefly deposit their offerings to the *Great Spirit* or *Father of Life.*

This has caused some to believe, that these Manitous are the objects that they worship, but that opinion is erroneous. The Indians believe that the Great Spirit either inhabits, or frequently visits, these manifestations of his power ; and that offerings deposited there, will sooner attract his notice, and gain his auspices, than in any other place. These offerings are propitiatory, either for success in war or in hunting, and consist of various articles, of which the feathers of the war eagle* are in the greatest estimation. On these rocks, several rude figures have been drawn by the Indians, with red paint ; they are chiefly in imitation of buffaloe, deer, &c. one of these, according with their idea of the Great Spirit, is not unlike our common representation of the devil. We encamped this night a little above the mouth of the Bonne Femme, a small river on the north side, where the tract of land, called Boond's Lick settlement, commences, supposed to be the best land in Western America for so great an area ; it extends about 150 miles up the Missouri, and is near 50 miles in breadth.

28th.—I left the boats early, intending to walk to the Lick settlements, which are the last on the river, excepting those occupied by one or two families near Fort Osage. After travelling eight or

---

* Falco melanætos.

C

ten miles, I was surprised in the woods by a severe thunder storm ; not knowing whether I could reach the settlements before night, I returned to meet the boat, and found our two hunters, who had sheltered themselves in a hollow tree. They had killed a buck, on a part of which we dined, and carried the remainder to the boat, and we arrived at the first house, belonging to a planter, named Hibband.— This evening we had a most tremendous thunder storm ; and about nine o'clock, a tree, not more than fifty yards from our camp, was shivered by lightning. Mr. Hunt, Mr. Nuttall, and myself, who were sitting in the tent, sensibly felt the action of the electric fluid.

29th.—As Mr. Hunt had some business with one of the settlers, we walked to his house, where we heard that war had already commenced between the Osages and the confederate nations, and that the former had killed seven of the Ayauways. This determined us to continue our practice of sleeping on our arms, as we had done since the 21st. We slept this night about a league above the settlements.

30th.—We were now beyond all the settlements, except those at Fort Osage, and Mr. Hunt resolved to send the hunters out more frequently, as game might now be expected in abundance. I accompanied them, and we killed a buck and a doe. I found the country, three or four miles from the river, very broken or stony. The almost incessant rains had now raised the Missouri to within a few feet of its annual flood, which rendered the navigation very difficult.

31st.—The morning was rainy, and was succeeded by a strong north wind, which caused a sudden change in the temperature of the weather: the 30th had been warm, but this night, the water in a tin cup of a pint measure that had been left full in the boat, was found to be nearly all solid ice, on the morning of the first of April.

April 1st.—After breakfast I went ashore with the two hunters, Harrington and Mears, but soon separated from them in order to visit the bluffs.— In the evening I descended into the valley, and on my way to find the boat, observed a skunk,* (*Viver-*

---

* This animal in its defence discharges a few drops of a liquid so fœtid, that the stench can scarcely be endured by any animal. Clothes on which the smallest particle has fallen, must be buried in the earth for at least a month before they can be worn. This liquor is highly inflamable, and is secreted in a gland beneath the tail, from which it is thrown with a force that will carry it to the distance of three or four yards. Only a very few of the American dogs can be induced to attack it, and those are so powerfully affected by the horrid stench, that they continue to

ra mephitis) and being desirous of procuring the skin, fired at it, but with shot only, having that day taken out my fowling-piece instead of my rifle. It appeared that I had either missed entirely, or only slightly wounded it, as it turned round instantly, and ran towards me. Being well aware of the consequence if overtaken, I fled, but was so closely pursued, that I was under the necessity of reloading whilst in the act of running. At the next discharge I killed it, but as it had ejected its offensive liquor upon its tail, I could not touch it, but cut a slender vine, of which I made a noose, and dragged my prize to the boat. I found that the Canadians considered it as a delicacy, and were desirous of procuring it to eat; this enabled me to obtain the skin without having to perform the disgusting operation of taking it off myself. Soon after my arrival, Harrington came in, and brought the intelligence that they had killed a large bear about four miles off. He had left Mears engaged in skinning it, and came to request that one or two men might be sent to assist in fetching it in. As it was near night, Mr. Hunt determined to stop, and two of the Canadians were sent along with Harrington, I also accompanied them. Al-

---

howl for a considerable time afterwards, and instinctively relieve themselves by scratching holes in the earth, into which they put their nose.

though our course lay through a very thick wood, Harrington led us with great precision towards the place, and when he supposed himself near it, he stopped, and we gave a shout. In a few seconds afterwards, we heard the discharge of a rifle, and also a shout from Mears, who was within two hundred yards of us. On joining him we were surprized to find that he had two bears. He informed us, that after the departure of Harrington he reloaded his rifle and laid it beside him whilst he was skinning and cutting up the bear,—he had nearly completed this operation, when he heard a rustling, as if an animal was coming towards him. To defend himself, he seized his piece, and at the moment we shouted, a bear appeared in view. Not seeing Mears, he laid his fore paws on the trunk of a fallen tree, and turned his head to look back: Mears could not have wished for a better opportunity, he shot him through the head. The bears were very large, and as the night had set in before the latter was skinned and cut up, it was too late to send to the boat for assistance; I therefore offered to carry a part, provided they would allot to me the skins, as they were the only clean part of the spoil; this proposition was agreed to, and we set out. Before we had proceeded far, it became quite dark, which caused us to take a wrong direction, that led to a swamp. In addition to our difficulties, the underwood consisted chiefly of the prickly ash,* by which our faces and hands were continually scratched: there was also an abundance of small prickly vines entwined among the bushes, of a species of *smilax*. These were easily avoided during day-light, but they were now almost every instant throwing some of us down. Whilst we were deliberating whether it would not be advisable to stop, make a fire, and remain there during the night, we heard the report of a gun, which we thought proceeded from the boat: we therefore steered our course in the direction of the sound; shortly afterwards we perceived before us a light glimmering through the trees, and in less than half an hour we had a full view of it. Mr. Hunt, from our long delay, had become apprehensive of what had really happened, viz. that we had lost our way, and having observed near the camp a very large cotton-wood tree, which was dead, and evidently hollow, he caused a hole to be cut into the cavity near the root, and a quantity of dry weeds being put in, it was set on fire. The trunk was at least seventy or eighty feet in length before the broken limbs commenced, several of these projected eight or ten feet, and were also hollow; the flames, impelled by so long a column of rarefied air, issued from the top, and from the ends of the limbs, with a surprising force,

---

* Zanthoxylon clava Hercules.

and with a noise equal to that of a blast furnace. Although smarting with pain, weary, wet, and hungry, not having eaten any thing since morning, I sat down to enjoy the scene, and have seldom witnessed one more magnificent. On relating to the hunters this evening, that I had been pursued by a skunk, they laughed heartily, and said it was no uncommon thing, having been often in the same predicament themselves.

2nd.—We this day passed the scite of a village on the north-east side of the river, once belonging to the Missouri tribe. Four miles above it are the remains of Fort Orleans, formerly belonging to the French ; it is 240 miles from the mouth of the Missouri. We passed the mouth of La Grande Riviere, near which I first observed the appearance of prairie,* on the alluvion of the river. Our hunters went out, but soon returned without attempting to kill any thing, having heard some shots

---

* Prairie is the term given to such tracts of land as are divested of timber. In travelling west from the Alleghanies they occur more frequently, and are of greater extent as we approach the Mississippi. When we proceed to the distance of two or three hundred miles west of that river, the whole country is of this description, which continues to the rocky mountains westward, and from the head waters of the Mississippi, to near the Gulf of Mexico; an extent of territory which probably equals in area the whole empire of China.

fired, which they discovered proceeded from Indians in pursuit of elk. The navigation had been very difficult for some days, on account of the frequent occurrence of what is termed by the boatmen *embarras.* They are formed by large trees falling into the river, where it has undermined the banks; some of these trees remain still attached by their roots to the firm ground, and the drift-wood being collected by the branches, a dam of the length of the tree is formed, round the point of which the water runs with such velocity, that in many instances it is impossible to stem it. On account of these obstacles, we were frequently under the necessity of crossing the river. This day the carcasses of several drowned buffaloes passed us.

3rd.—I walked the greatest part of the day, but found it troublesome, being much annoyed by the prickly ash. In the evening we had another severe thunder storm.

4th.—The navigation became less difficult, as the river had fallen four feet.

5th.—Went out with the hunters, who shot nothing but a goose, *(Anas Canadensis)* that was sitting on a tree beside its nest, on which was the female. Observed for the first time that the rocks bordering the river were sand-stone. In these I found nodules of iron ore imbedded.

'6th.—Walked all day, and in the afternoon met the hunters, who had found a bee tree,* and were returning to the boat for a bucket, and a hatchet to cut it down. I accompanied them to the tree. It contained a great number of combs, and about three gallons of honey. The honey bees have been introduced into this continent from Europe, but at what time I have not been able to ascertain. Even if it be admitted that they were brought over soon after the first settlement took place, their increase since appears astonishing, as bees are found in all parts of the United States; and since they have entered upon the fine countries of the Illinois and Upper Louisiana, their progress westward has been surprisingly rapid. It is generally known in Upper Louisiana, that bees had not been found westward of the Mississippi prior to the year 1797.† They are now found as high up the Missouri as the Maha nation, having moved westward to the distance of 600 miles in 14 years. Their extraordinary

---

* The term given in America to a hollow tree, containing a swarm of bees.

† At that time the natural history of the bee was not very well known at St. Louis. They relate there, that a French lady of that place having received a present of honey from Kaskaskias, was much delighted with it, and being told it was produced by a kind of fly, she sent a negro with a small box to Kaskaskias (60 miles) to get a pair of the flies, in order that she might obtain the breed.

progress in these parts is probably owing to a portion of the country being prairie, and yielding therefore a succession of flowers during the whole summer, which is not the case in forests. Bees have spread over this continent in a degree and with a celerity so nearly corresponding with that of the Anglo-Americans, that it has given rise to a belief, both amongst the Indians and the whites, that bees are their precursors, and that to whatever part they go the white people will follow. I am of opinion that they are right, as I think it as impossible to stop the progress of the one as of the other. We encamped this night at the bottom of an island.

7th.—This morning I went upon the island, accompanied by one of the Frenchmen named Guardepee, to look for game. We were wholly unsuccessful in our pursuit, although the island is of considerable extent. On arriving at the upper end of it, we perceived a small island, of about two acres, covered with grass only, and separated from the large one by a narrow channel, the mouth of which was covered with drift timber. We passed over, and walked through the grass, and having given up all hopes of game, we were proceeding to the river to wait for the boat, when suddenly my companion, who was before me, stopped, fired, and jumped aside, crying out, " *Voila O diable, tirez,*" at the same time pointing towards the grass a few steps before him. I looked, and saw a bear not five yards from us. I immediately fired, and we retired to a short distance to reload, but on our return found the animal expiring. It was a female, with three small cubs in her bed, about two yards from where she was killed. She had heard us approach, and was advancing to defend them. I took one of the cubs in my arms. It seemed sensible of its misfortune, and cried at intervals. It was evident that whenever it uttered a cry the convulsions of the dying mother increased, and I really felt regret that we had so suddenly cut the ties of so powerful an affection.* Whilst we breakfasted the bear was cut up, and, with the young ones, taken on board. We encamped this night about twelve miles below Fort Osage.

8th.—About ten o'clock we came in sight of the fort, about six miles distant. We had not been long

---

* The great attachment which the she bear has for her young is well known to the American hunter. No danger can induce her to abandon them. Even when they are sufficiently grown to be able to climb a tree, her anxiety for their safety is but little diminished. At that time, if hunted and attacked by dogs, her first care is to make her young climb to a place of safety. If they show any reluctance, she beats them, and having succeeded, turns fearlessly on her pursuers. Perhaps in animal economy maternal affection is almost always commensurate with the helplessness of the young.

in sight before we saw the flag was hoisted, and at
noon we arrived, saluting with a volley as we passed on to the landing place, where we met Mr.
Crooks, who had come down from the wintering
station at the mouth of the river Naduet to meet
us. There were also collected at the landing place
about 200 Indians, men, women, and children, of
the Petit Osage nation, whose village was then a-
bout 300 yards from the fort. We passed through
them to pay our respects to Lieutenant Brownson,
who then commanded in the absence of Captain
Clemson. He received us very politely, and insisted that we should eat at his table during our
stay. I had with me an introductory letter to Dr.
Murray, physician to the garrison, whom I found
disposed to give me every information relative to
the customs and manners of the Osage nation, and
from him also I received a vocabulary of a considerable number of words in that language.* He
walked with me down to the boats, where we found
a number of squaws assembled, as Dr. Murray assured me, for the same purpose as females of a certain class in the maritime towns of Europe crowd
round vessels lately arrived from a long voyage,
and it must be admitted with the same success.
Towards evening an old chief came down, and harangued the Indians assembled about the boats, for

* See Appendix, No. I.

the purpose of inviting the warriors of the late expedition to a feast prepared for them in the village. I was told it was intended that the dance of the scalp should be performed on the occasion of the war party having brought in seven scalps from the Ayauwais, a village belonging to whom they had destroyed, and killed two old men and five women and children. All the rest had fled at their approach ; but as rain came on the dance was not performed. At evening Dr. Murray proposed that we should walk into the village, and I found it to consist of about one hundred lodges of an oblong form, the frame of timber, and the covering mats, made of the leaves of flag, or *Typha palustris.* On our return through the town, we called at the lodge belonging to a chief named Waubuschon, with whom Dr. Murray was particularly acquainted. The floor was covered with mats, on which they sat ; but as I was a stranger, I was offered a cushion. A wooden bowl was now handed round, containing square pieces of cake, in taste resembling gingerbread. On enquiry I found it was made of the pulp of the persimon,* mixed with pounded corn. This bread they called staninca. Shortly afterwards some young squaws came in, with whom the doctor (who understood the Osage language) began to joke, and in a few minutes they seemed to have overcome all bashfulness,

---

* Diospyros Virginiana.

or even modesty. Some of their expressions, as interpreted to me, were of the most obscene nature. The squaw of our host laughed heartily, and did all in her power to promote this kind of conversation. I expressed my surprise to Dr. Murray, but was informed by him that similar conduct would have been pursued at any other lodge in the village. We left the lodge of Waubuschon, and went to that of the chief. On the roof the seven scalps were placed, tied to sticks ornamented with racoon tails. We were shewn to the upper end of the lodge, and sat down on the ground. I learned that the chief was not present; that he was a boy of six years of age, his name Young White Hair, and that the tribe was now governed by a regent. Immediately a warrior came in, and made a speech, frequently pointing to the scalps on the roof, as they were visible through the hole that admitted the smoke to pass. I understood that he had distinguished himself in the late expedition against the Ayauways. After shaking hands with all round, we left the lodge, and in our return to the boat we met the squaw belonging to our interpreter, who being of the Ayauway nation, appeared to be much afraid of the Osages during our passage up the river, and it was thought with reason, as on our first interview with the commandant, it had been debated whether or not it would be prudent to send a file of men to conduct her from the boat to the fort during our stay. On enquiry we found that

she had been invited up to the village by some of
the Osages, and of course, according to Indian
custom, would be as safe with them as in the fort.

I enquired of Dr. Murray concerning a practice
which I had heard prevailed amongst the Osages,
of rising before day to lament their dead. He informed me that such was really the custom, and
that the loss of a horse or a dog was as powerful a
stimulus to their lamentations as that of a relative
or friend; and he assured me, that if I should be
awake before day the following morning, I might
certainly hear them. Accordingly on the 9th I
heard before day that the howling had commenced;
and the better to escape observation, I wrapped a
blanket round me, tied a black handkerchief on my
head, and fastened on my belt, in which I stuck my
tomahawk, and then walked into the village. The
doors of the lodges were closed, but in the greater
part of them the women were crying and howling
in a tone that seemed to indicate excessive grief.
On the outside of the village I heard the men who
Dr. Murray had informed me always go out of the
lodges to lament. I soon came within twenty paces
of one, and could see him distinctly, as it was moon-
light: he also saw me and ceased, upon which I withdrew. I was more successful with another, whom
I approached nearer unobserved. He rested his
back against the stump of a tree, and continued for

about twenty seconds to cry out in a loud and high tone of voice, when he suddenly lowered to a low muttering, mixed with sobs : in a few seconds he again raised to the former pitch.* We breakfasted with the commandant, and afterwards walked out to view some improvements he had made in the fort. In our walk we observed what, on the first view appeared to be two squaws carrying a tub of water, suspended on a pole. Mr. Crooks desired me to notice them, which I did, and remarked that one of them had more the appearance of a man than of a woman. He assured me that it was a man, and that there were several others in the village, who, like the one we saw, were condemned for life to associate with the squaws, to wear the same dress, and do the same drudgery. I now learned, that when the Osages go to war, they keep a watchful eye over the young men who are then making their first essay in arms, and such as appear to possess the necessary qualifications are admitted to the rank of warriors, or, according to their own idiom, *brave men.* But if any exhibit evident proofs of cowardice, on the return of the party they are

---

* I have been informed, that when the Osages were in the habit of robbing the white settlers, it was customary with them, after they had entered the house, and before they proceeded to plunder, to blacken their faces, and cry. The reason they gave for this was, that they were sorry for the people whom they were going to rob.

compelled to assume the dress and character of women, and their doom is fixed for life, as no opportunity
is afterwards afforded them to retrieve their character.* The men do not associate with them, nor are
they suffered to marry, or have any intercourse with
the women: they may be treated with the greatest in-
dignity by any warrior, as they are not suffered to resent it. I found, on enquiry, that the late war party
had not been conducted by any of the principal chiefs,
a circumstance which often happens, as any of the
noted warriors may lead a party, provided he can obtain adherents, and he finds no difficulty in procuring the sanction of the chiefs; but in this case he
must travel without mockasons, or even leggings.
He goes the foremost of the party, makes the fire at

---

* It is customary amongst the Missouri Indians to register
every exploit in war, by making a notch for each on the handle
of their tomahawks, and they are estimated as being rich or poor
in proportion to the number of notches. At their war dances,
any warrior who chuses may recount his exploits. This is done
by pointing to each notch, and describing the particular act that
entitled him to it. The Nodowessies, or Sioux, fix up a post
near the war fire, to represent the enemy of each warrior in succession whilst he is recounting his deeds. During his harangue
he strikes the post when in the act of describing how he struck
his enemy, and, like Alexander, "fights his battles o'er again."
Mr. Crooks informed me, that the day before our arrival at the
fort he saw an Osage beating and kicking another, who suffered
it patiently. Mr. Crooks asked him why he did not defend himself? " Oh!" said he, shewing the handle of his tomahawk,
" *I am too poor ; he is richer than I am.*"

night, and stands to keep watch whilst the party lie down to sleep, nor can he lie down unless a warrior rises and takes his place. This indulgence he must not require, but may accept, if voluntarily offered. In pursuing the object of the expedition his commands are absolute, and he is obeyed without a murmur. The Osages are so tall and robust as almost to warrant the application of the term gigantic: few of them appear to be under six feet, and many are above it. Their shoulders and visages are broad, which tends to strengthen the idea of their being giants. On our return from viewing the improvements in the fort, I was introduced to Mr. Sibly, the Indian agent there, who is the son of Dr. Sibly of Natchitoches. He informed me that he purposed shortly to attend the Petits Osages in their annual journey for salt. He invited me to accompany him, and as an inducement, offered to procure two horses from the Indians for my own use. Learning that the place where the salt is procured is that which has occasioned the report of a salt mountain existing in Upper Louisiana, I was very much inclined to accept his invitation; but finding Mr. Hunt unwilling to release me from my promise to attend him, I declined it. I accompanied Mr. Sibly and Dr. Murray in the evening, to see the dance of the scalp. The ceremony consisted in carrying the scalps elevated on sticks through the village, followed by the warriors who had composed the war party, dressed in all their ornaments, and painted as for war.

On the 10th we again embarked on the river, although it rained very hard. Our number was now augmented to twenty-six by the addition of Mr. Crooks and his party. We had not proceeded more than two miles when our interpreter, Dorion, beat his squaw severely; and on Mr. Hunt enquiring the cause, he told him that she had taken a fancy to remain at the Osages in preference to proceeding with us, and because he had opposed it, she had continued sulky ever since. We were obliged to encamp early this day, as the rain became excessive.

11th, 12th, 13th, and 14th.—We had a fair wind, and employed our sail, wherefore I could not go ashore without danger of being left behind. During these days the bread was examined, and being found wholly unfit for use, it was thrown overboard.

15th.—We passed the scite of a village which formerly belonged to the Kansas Indians. I had an opportunity of going ashore, and found the soil to have the appearance of the greatest fertility. On the sides of the hills I noticed abundance of the hop plant, *(Humulus lupulus.)*

16th.—We began to notice more particularly the great number of the bodies of drowned buffaloes, floating on the river; vast numbers of them were also thrown ashore, and upon the rafts, on the points of the Islands. These carcasses had attracted an immense number of turkey buzzards, *(Vultur aura)* and as the preceding night had been rainy, multitudes of them were sitting on the trees, with their backs towards the sun, and their wings spread out to dry, a common practice with these birds, after rain.

17th.—Arrived at the wintering houses, near the Naduet river, and joined the rest of the party.

18th.—I proceeded to examine the neighbouring country, and soon discovered that pigeons* were in the woods. I returned, and exchanged my rifle for a fowling piece, and in a few hours shot 271, when I desisted. I had an opportunity this day of observing the manner in which they feed; it affords a most singular spectacle, and is also an example of the rigid discipline maintained by gregarious animals. This species of pigeon associates in prodigious flocks: one of these flocks, when on the ground, will cover an area of several acres in extent, and are so close to each other that the ground can scarcely be seen. This phalanx moves through

---

* Columbo migratorius.

the woods with considerable celerity, picking up as it passes along, every thing that will serve for food. It is evident that the foremost ranks must be the most successful, and that nothing will remain for the hindermost. That all may have an equal chance, the instant that any rank becomes the last, they rise, and flying over the whole flock, alight exactly ahead of the foremost. They succeed each other with so much rapidity, that there is a continued stream of them in the air; and a side view of them exhibits the appearance of the segment of a large circle, moving through the woods. I observed that they cease to look for food a considerable time before they become the last rank, but strictly adhere to their regulations, and never rise until there are none behind them.

19th.—On the bluffs* under which the winter-

---

* As the term bluff may not be understood, an explanation will render the application more intelligible. The alluvion of the great rivers west of the Alleghannies is considerably lower than the surrounding country, and is of a breadth nearly in the ratio of the magnitude of the river ; that of the Missouri is from two to six or eight miles in breadth, and is for the most part from 150 to 300 feet below the general level of the country. The ascent from this valley into the country is precipitous, and is called "the Bluff;" it may consist of rock or clay. Betwixt these bluffs the river runs in a very crooked channel, and is perpetually changing its bed, as the only permanent bounds are the bluffs. It may here be remarked, that a view of the vast

ing house was placed, are a considerable number of flat stones. On examining one, I found beneath it several snakes, in a half torpid state, arising probably from the cold state of the weather, and found on farther examination, that the number of snakes under these stones was astonishing. I selected this day eleven species, and killed a great number.

20th.—It was this day arranged, by the desire of Mr. Donald M'Kenzie, that I should travel in his boat, and preparations were made for our departure the succeeding morning. I was employed in continuing my researches, and had a narrow escape from a rattle-snake; it darted at me from the top of a small rock, at the base of which I was gathering plants. The noise of its rattle just gave me sufficient notice to withdraw my head.

21st.—We again embarked in four boats. Our party amounted to nearly sixty persons: forty were Canadian boatmen, such as are employed by the North West Company, and are termed in Canada *Engagés* or *Voyageurs.* Our boats were all

---

channel bounded by these bluffs, connected with the idea that all which it contained has been carried away by the river, would induce us to believe that this globe has existed longer than *some people* imagine.

furnished with masts and sails, and as the wind blew pretty strong from the south-east, we availed ourselves of it during the most part of the day.

22nd, 23rd, and 24th.—The wind continuing favourable, we sailed almost the whole of these three days, and made considerable progress.

25th.—Went ashore with the hunters, and collected a new species of rattle-snake, and a bird of the genus *Recurvirostra*. The hunters killed two elks, but they were so lean that we left them for the vultures : at all times their flesh is much inferior to that of the deer.

26th.—The wind had changed to the north west, and blew so strong, that we were obliged to stop during the whole day. When I found this measure determined on, I resolved to avail myself of the opportunity to quit the valley of the Missouri, and examine the surrounding country. After travelling about three miles, I ascended the bluffs, and found that the face of the country, soil, &c. were entirely changed. As far as the eye could reach, not a single tree or shrub was visible. The whole of the stratum immediately below the vegetable mould, is a vast bed of exceedingly hard yellow clay. In the valleys, the land floods, during the rainy season, have worn channels so deep, and with the sides so precipitous, that a traveller is often under the necessity of proceeding a mile or two along one of these ravines before he can cross it.. In the bottoms of several I observed evident indications of coal.

27th.—The night had been very cold, and before we had been long on the river, the sides of the boats and the oars were covered with ice, although we were not farther north than 40°. After break-fast, I went out with the hunters, and found my hopes of a change in the vegetation realized. The bluffs forming the bounds of the river are no longer in part rocks, but a continued chain of rounded knobs of stiff clay; under these is a fine bed of bituminous coal, rendered visible wherever the river has washed away the base. This day I col-lected several new species of plants.

28th.—We breakfasted on one of the islands formed by La Platte Riviere, the largest river that falls into the Missouri. It empties itself into three channels, except in the time of its annual flood, when the intervening land is overflowed; it is then about a mile in breadth. We noticed this day the skeleton or frame of a skin canoe, in which the river had been crossed by Indians: we saw also other indications of war parties having been re-cently in the neighbourhood, and observed in the night the reflection of immense fires, occasioned by burning the prairies. At this late season, the fires are not made by the hunters to facilitate their hunting, but by war parties; and more particularly when returning unsuccessful, or after a defeat, to prevent their enemies from tracing their steps. As the ash discontinues to grow on the Missouri above this place, it was thought expedient to lay in a stock of oars and poles; and for that purpose, we stopped in the forenoon, about a league above the mouth of Papillon Creek, and I availed myself of this opportunity to visit the bluffs four or five miles distant from us, on the north east side. On approaching them, I found an extensive lake running along their base, across which I waded, the water in no part reaching higher than my breast. This lake had evidently been in former times the course of the river: its surface was much covered with aquatic plants, amongst which were *Nelumbium luteum* and *Hydropeltis purpurea;* on the broad leaves of the former, a great number of water snakes were basking, which on my approach darted into the water. On gaining the summit of the bluffs, I was amply repaid by the grandeur of the scene that suddenly opened to my view, and by the acquisition of a number of new plants. On looking into the valley of the Missouri from an elevation of about 250 feet, the view was magnificent; the bluffs can be seen for more than thirty miles, stretching to the north-eastward in a right line, their summits varied by an infinity of undulations. The flat valley of the river, about six or seven miles in breadth, is partly prairie, but interspersed with clumps of the finest trees, through the intervals of which could be seen the majestic but muddy Missouri. The scene towards the interior of the country was extremely singular: it presents to the view a countless number of little green hills, apparently sixty or eighty feet in perpendicular height, and so steep, that it was with much difficulty I could ascend them; some were so acutely pointed, that two people would have found it difficult to stand on the top at the same time. I wandered among these mountains in miniature until late in the afternoon, when I recrossed the lake, and arrived at the boats soon after sunset.

29th.—Being informed that the oars and poles would not be finished before noon, Mr. M'Kenzie obliged me by sending his boat to carry me across the river. I found the bluffs to be of a nature similar to those on the north-east side. I met the boats in the afternoon, and we encamped about fourteen miles below the wintering house belonging to Mr. Crooks, who proposed to me that we should walk to it the following morning, along the bluffs; as that route was much shorter than by the course of the river.

30th.—I set out with Mr. Crooks at sunrise, for the wintering house, and travelled nearly a mile on a low piece of ground, covered with long grass; at its termination we ascended a small elevation, and entered on a plain of about eight miles in length, and from two and a half to three miles in breadth. As the old grass had been burned in the autumn, it was now covered with the most beautiful verdure, intermixed with flowers. It was also adorned with clumps of trees, sufficient for ornament, but too few to intercept the sight: in the intervals we counted nine flocks of elk and deer feeding, some of which we attempted to approach near enough to fire at, but without success. On arriving at the termination of the plain, our route lay along a series of the most rugged clay bluffs: some of them were in part washed away by the river, and exhibited perpendicular faces at least a hundred feet in height. At noon we arrived at the wintering house, and dined on dried buffaloe. In the evening the boats came up.

May 1st.—This day was employed in embarking some articles necessary for the voyage, together with Indian goods, and in the evening Mr. Crooks informed me that he intended to set out the next morning on foot, for the Ottoes, a nation of Indians on the Platte river, who owed him some beaver. From the Ottoes he purposed travelling to the Maha nation, about 200 miles above us on the Missouri, where he should again meet the boats. I immediately offered to accompany him, he seemed much pleased, and we proceeded to cast bullets, and make other arrangements necessary for our journey.

2nd.—At day-break we were preparing to depart, as also were the rest of the party, when an occurrence took place that delayed us until sunrise, and created a considerable degree of confusion. Amongst our hunters were two brothers of the name of Harrington, one of whom, Samuel Harrington, had been hunting on the Missouri for two years, and had joined the party in Autumn: the other, William Harrington, had engaged at St. Louis, in the following March, and accompanied us from thence; the latter now avowed that he had engaged at the command of his mother, for the purpose of bringing back his brother, and they both declared their intention of abandoning the party immediately. As it had already been intimated to us at the Osage nation, that the Nodowessie, or Sioux Indians, intended to oppose our progress up the river, and as no great dependance was placed on our Canadians in case of an attack, the loss of two good riflemen was a matter of regret to us all. Mr. Hunt, although a gentleman of the mildest disposition, was ex-

tremely exasperated ; and when it was found that all
arguments and entreaties were unavailing, they were
left, as it was then imagined, without a single bullet or a load of powder, 400 miles at least from any
white man's house, and 650 from the mouth of the
river. As soon as the final issue of this affair was
known, Mr. Crooks and myself set out for the Otto
village, attended by two of the Canadians, one
named Guardépée, the other La Liberté. Our
equipments were, a blanket, a rifle, eighty bullets,
a full powder horn, a knife, and tomahawk, for each.
Besides these, I had a large inflexible port-folio,
containing several quires of paper, for the purpose
of laying down specimens of plants ; we had also a
small camp-kettle, and a little jerked buffaloe meat.
In half an hour we left the valley of the Missouri,
and entered upon the vast plain. We took our
course S. S. E. which we held for some hours,
and travelled at a great rate, hoping to reach the
Platte that night, although estimated at forty-five
miles from the place of our departure. A little
before noon we saw four large animals at a great
distance, which we supposed to be elk, but on
crossing their footsteps some time afterwards, we
found to our great satisfaction that they were buffaloe.
In the afternoon we crossed two branches of Papillon Creek, and an hour before sun-set arrived
at the Corne du Cerf River, a deep clear stream,
about eighty yards in breadth, it falls into the

Platte, about twenty miles below. As our Canadians could not swim, it was necessary to construct
a raft, and we concluded to remain here for the
night. This arrangement was very agreeable to
me, as I was much exhausted, which Mr. Crooks
considered was, in a great measure, owing to my
having drank water too copiously during the day.
Although we had not eaten anything from the time
of our departure, I was unable to eat at supper,
and lay down immediately.

3rd.—We arose at day break. I found myself completely refreshed. Our raft being ready at sun-rise, we crossed the river, and in two
hours arrived at the Platte, exactly opposite the
Otto village. The river is here about 800 yards
in breadth, but appears to be shallow, as its name
indicates. The southern bank is wholly divested
of timber, and as the village is situated on a declivity near the river, we could see the lodges very
distinctly, but there was no appearance of Indians.
We discharged our rifles, but the signal was not answered from the village; in about five minutes we
heard the report of a gun down the river, and immediately proceeded towards the place. At the
distance of half a mile, we arrived opposite an
island, on the point of which a white man was
standing, who informed us that we could cross
over to him by wading; we did not stop to take
off our clothes, but went over immediately, the

water reaching to our arm-pits. This man proved to be an American, of the name of Rogers, and was employed as an interpreter by a Frenchman from St. Louis, who was also on the island with a few goods. They informed us that they had been concealed for some days on the island, having discovered a war party hovering round, belonging, as they supposed, to the Loup, or Wolf nation, who had come in order to surprise the Ottoes. They had nothing to give us as food, excepting some beaver flesh, which Rogers obtained by trapping on Corne du Cerf, or Elk Horn river; as it was stale, and tasted fishy, I did not much relish it, but there was no alternative but to eat it or starve. We remained all day concealed on the island, and on the morning of the 4th, before daylight, Rogers set out to look at his traps, on Elk Horn river, distant to the Eastward not more than five miles. I accompanied him, and on crossing the channel of the Platte, found that in the same place where the day before it reached to our arm-pits, it did not now reach to our waists, although the river had not fallen; such changes in the bottom of this river, Rogers told me were very frequent, as it is composed of a moving gravel, in which our feet sunk to a considerable depth. We arrived at the Elk Horn river about sun-rise, but found no beaver in the traps. After our return to the island, I expressed a wish to visit the Otto village, which was in sight; and Rogers, who had a canoe concealed in the willows that surrounded the island, landed me on the other side of the river. I found the village to consist of about fifty-four lodges, of a circular form, and about forty feet in diameter, with a projecting part at the entrance, of ten or twelve feet in length, in the form of a porch. At almost every lodge, the door or entrance was closed after the manner which is customary with Indians when they go on hunting parties and take their squaws and children with them. It consists in putting a few sticks across, in a particular manner, which they so exactly note and remember, as to be able to discover the least change in their position. Although anxious to examine the internal structure of the lodges, I did not violate the injunction conveyed by this slight obstruction, and after searching some time found a few that were left entirely open. On entering one, I found the length of the porch to be an inclined plane to the level of the floor, about two and a half or three feet below the surface of the ground; round the area of the lodge are placed from fifteen to eighteen posts, forked at the top, and about seven feet high from the floor. In the centre, a circular space of about eight feet in diameter is dug, to the depth of two feet; four strong posts are placed in the form of a square, about twelve feet asunder, and at equal distances from this space; these posts are about twenty feet high, and cross pieces are laid on the tops. The rafters are laid from the forked tops of the outside posts over these cross pieces, and reach nearly to the centre, where a small hole is left for the smoke to escape : across the rafters small pieces of timber are laid ; over these, sticks and a covering of sods, and lastly earth. The fire is made in the middle of the central space, round the edges of which they sit, and the beds are fixed betwixt the outer posts. The door is placed at the immediate entrance into the lodge ; it is made of a buffaloe skin, stretched in a frame of wood, and is suspended from the top. On entering, it swings forward, and when let go, it falls to its former position. On my return to the island, Mr. Crooks informed me that he had resolved to send Rogers to find the Ottoes, who were hunting about twenty miles from us, in order to collect his debts, or to procure horses for us, to facilitate our journey to the Maha nation.

5th.—In the morning early, Rogers set out on his expedition, and nothing material occurred until his return on the 6th, without his having obtained any beaver or horses, excepting one belonging to Mr. Crooks. This night I procured from Rogers what information I could relative to the Otto nation, and was informed that the Missouris are incorporated with them, from whom they are de-

scended, and whose language they speak. They
call themselves Wad-doké-tăh-tăh, and can muster
130 or 140 warriors. They were now at war with
the Loups, or Wolf Indians, the Osages, and the
Sioux. He said they furnish a considerable quantity of bear, deer, and beaver skins, and are very
well disposed towards their traders, who may safely
credit them. They do not claim the property of
the land on which they live, nor any other tract. A
very considerable part of the surrounding country
formerly belonged to the Missouris, who were once
the most powerful nation on the Missouri river,
but have been reduced by war and the small pox
to be dependent on the Ottoes, by whom they are
treated as inferiors. Rogers had with him a squaw
of the Maha nation, with her child, whom he wished to send with us to her father. To this Mr.
Crooks consented, and early on the morning of the
7th we set out, putting the squaw and her child on
the horse. Having crossed over from the island,
we steered a due North course, and came to the
Elk Horn river, after travelling about ten miles.
Mr. Crooks immediately stripped, to examine if
the river was fordable, and found that, excepting
about twenty yards in the middle, we might wade
it. I offered to carry the child, but the squaw refused, and after stripping herself, she gave me her
clothes, put the child on her neck, and swam over,
the little creature sticking to her hair. After as-

sisting our Canadians across, we continued along the bank, in the expectation of arriving at a creek, distant about five miles, which comes in a direction from the North. We had observed, that as we increased our distance from the island, the reluctance of the squaw to proceed also increased, and soon after we had crossed the river, she began to cry, and declared she would go no farther. Mr. Crooks, who understood the language, remonstrated with her ; but finding it in vain, he ordered Guardepée to take her back, and we encamped to wait his return.

8th.—About two o'clock in the morning Guardepée returned with the horse, and at day-light we set out. In about an hour we came to the creek, and continued along its banks, and found ourselves in a short time on a most beautiful prairie, along which the creek flowed, without having a single tree on its border, or even a shrub, excepting a few widely scattered plum bushes. We shot this day two prairie hens, *(Tetrao umbellus)* on which we supped, having dined on some jerked buffalo, brought by Rogers from the Ottoes. We slept on the border of the creek, but not so comfortably as usual, as the dew was so copious, that before morning our blankets were wet through.

9th.—We continued to pursue our course along

the creek, but with great trouble, as our mockassons, being of untanned skins, became so soft as to
render it difficult to keep them on our feet. We
shot a prairie hen, and prepared to breakfast, having first relieved the horse from the baggage, and
turned him out to graze. Whilst we were collecting some dry stalks of plants to boil our kettle, a
herd of elk, nineteen in number, appeared marching towards the creek, and Guardepée immediately
ran to put himself in such a position that he might
fire at them, when the horse took fright, broke his
tie, and gallopped off. Guardepée fired, but only
wounded one so slightly that it ran off with the rest,
and escaped. The horse took the direct route back
towards the Ottoes, and was followed by Mr.
Crooks and Guardepée; but in vain : they gave up
the chase, finding it impossible to recover him.
After we had breakfasted, we threw the saddle and
every thing belonging to the horse into the creek;
each man took his share of the baggage, and we
again set out, and travelled without stopping until
evening, when we arrived at the head of the creek,
and came to what is called ɐ dividing ridge.* We
passed over it, and came to the head of a creek,
running in a N.E. direction. This we supposed
to be Black Bird Creek, which falls into the Mis-

---

* A term given to any elevation that separates the head waters
of one creek from those of another.

souri, near the monument of a famous chief of the
Mahas, named Black Bird. At the distance of
about two miles, we saw a small clump of trees on
the border of the creek, and determined to remain
there during the night, hoping to find fuel to boil
a small portion of jerked buffalo, being all we had
left. Whilst the supper was preparing, I walked
back to an eminence, to collect some interesting
plants, having noticed them in passing. I had not
been long employed in that way, when I saw a distant flash of lightning in the South, and soon after
others in quick succession. Other appearances
indicated the approach of a violent storm, and I
hastened back to recommend precautions for the
security of our arms and ammunition. Having
boiled our meat, which amounted to a few morsels
each, we secured our powder horns and some tow
in our camp kettle, which we inverted, and discharged our rifles. Excepting the sound of distant thunder, which was continual, an awful silence
prevailed, and the cloud which had already spread
over one half of the visible horizon, was fast shutting out the little remains of day-light. As the
trees afforded us no fuel, and in a few minutes
would become no shelter, but might endanger our
safety, I recommended that we should go to the
open prairie, which we did, and lay down in our
blankets; I put my plants under me. For several hours the thunder, lightning, and rain were

incessant, and such rain as I have seldom witnessed. In half an hour after the storm commenced, we had nothing more to fear from it, excepting the cold occasioned by the torrents that fell on us. At the approach of morning the rain ceased; we saw a few stars, and with joy noticed the first appearances of day. We rose, and wrung the water out of our blankets, and finding ourselves very much benumbed, we walked about to restore the circulation; when it was sufficiently light, we put our rifles in order, which was attended with considerable difficulty, as our hands were almost without sensation. Having arranged our arms we set out, but were extremely uncomfortable, as our clothes, being made of dressed skins, stuck so close to our bodies as to make our march very unpleasant. We proceeded at a brisk pace to warm ourselves, and in about two hours came to a small ridge, which we ascended, and when near the top, Guardepée preceded us, to examine if any game was in sight. He gave the signal for us to remain quiet, and soon afterwards fired at two buffaloe cows, with their calves; one of the cows he wounded, and they ran off with so much speed, that the calves could not keep up with them: perceiving this, I immediately pursued the calve, one of which I killed. The rest of the party pursued the cows for a short distance, but finding the inutility of it, they soon returned; and notwithstanding my remonstrances,

Guardepée killed the other calf. As we had eaten
but little the day before, we were very glad of
this supply, and taking what we thought proper,
proceeded on our journey. We soon began to perceive that the face of the country was changing
in its appearance. From the Elk Horn river, our
course had hitherto been over a most beautiful
prairie, with scarcely a tree or shrub, but covered
with grass and flowers; we now began to observe
a more broken country to the eastward, and some
scattered bushes in the vallies. From an eminence,
we soon after perceived a hill, having a heap of
stones on the summit; Mr. Crooks assured me that
this was the monument of Blackbird,* the famous

---

* This chief, called by the French, Oiseau Noir, ruled over
the Mahas with a sway the most despotic : he had managed in
such a manner as to inspire them with the belief that he was
possessed of supernatural powers ; in council no chief durst oppose him—in war it was death to disobey. It is related of him
at St. Louis, that a trader from that town arrived at the Mahas
with an assortment of Indian goods; he applied to Blackbird
for liberty to trade, who ordered that he should first bring all
his goods into his lodge, and the order was obeyed ; Blackbird
commanded that all the packages should be opened in his presence, and from them he selected what goods he thought proper,
amounting to nearly the fourth part of the whole ; he caused
them to be placed in a part of the lodge distinct from the rest,
and addressed the trader to this effect—" Now, my son, the
" goods which I have chosen are mine, and those in your
" possession are your own. Don't cry, my son, my people
" shall trade with you for your goods *at your own price.*"

Maha chief, and that it was one of the bluffs of the Missouri; we judged it was about fifteen miles N. E. of us. Satisfied that we were now near the boats, and having arrived at some small timber, where we could procure fuel, we dined on our veal; and although without bread or salt, it was to us a luxury, as we had long been unaccustomed to those articles. We halted about three hours before sunset, at about five miles from the monument of Blackbird, to which place Mr. Crooks dispatched Guardepee to look for a letter, as Mr.

He then spoke to his herald, who ascended to the top of the lodge, and commanded in the name of the chief, that the Mahas should bring all their beaver, bear, otter, muskrat, and other skins to his lodge, and not on any account to dispute the terms of exchange with the trader, who declared on his return to St. Louis, that it was the most profitable voyage he had ever made. Mr. Tellier, a gentleman of respectability who resided near St. Louis, and who had been formerly Indian agent there, informed me that Blackbird obtained this influence over his nation by the means of arsenic, a quantity of that article having been sold to him by a trader, who instructed him in the use of it. If afterwards, any of his nation dared to oppose him in his arbitary measures, he *prophesied* their death within a certain period, and took good care that his predictions should be verified. He died about the time that Louisiana was added to the United States; having previously made choice of a cave for his sepulchre, on the top of a hill near the Missouri, about eighteen miles below the Maha village; by his order his body was placed on the back of his favourite horse, which was driven into the cave, the mouth closed up with stones, and a large heap was afterwards raised on the summit of the hill.

Hunt had promised to leave one there on passing the place. At night he returned, but without a letter, and we concluded that the boats had not yet arrived.

11th.—We set off early, and soon fell in with the trace from the Maha village to the monument; along this we travelled, and about ten o'clock arrived at the town, where we met one of the Canadians belonging to the boats. He informed us that they arrived the day before, and were stationed about four miles from the village. As we were in want of food, we did not stop, but proceeded to the boats, where we found a considerable number of Indians assembled to trade. They gave jerked buffaloe meat, tallow, corn, and marrow; and in return they received tobacco in carottes, vermillion, blue beads, &c. There, also, we found Mr. James Aird, an old and respectable trader, whom I had become acquainted with at St. Louis. He informed me that he should go to the United States in a few days, I therefore availed myself of this opportunity to forward letters, and was employed in writing until the 12th at noon. Immediately after, I set out on an excursion to the bluffs, and in my way passed through the village, where the great number of children playing about the lodges, entirely naked immediately drew my attention. I soon attracted their notice also, and they began to collect around me; some of the boldest ventured to touch my hand, after which they ran back a few paces, but soon again resumed their courage. When about fifty or sixty had collected, I came to where three young squaws were repairing one of the stages erected for the purpose of exposing the buffaloe skins to dry, whilst they are in preparation. The squaws, seeing the children run after me, spoke to them, in a commanding tone, when they instantly stopped, and not one followed me afterwards. I doubt much if such a crowd of children, in any European city, would have obeyed with such promptness, had such a phenomenon appeared amongst them, as they must have considered me. On arriving at the summit of the bluffs, I had a fine view of the town below. It had a singular appearance; the frame work of the lodges consists of ten or twelve long poles, placed in the periphery of a circle of about sixteen feet in diameter, and are inclined towards each other, so as to cross at a little more than half their length from the bottom; and the tops diverging with the same angle, exhibit the appearance of one cone inverted on the apex of another. The lower cone is covered with dressed buffaloe skins, sewed together, and fancifully painted; some with an undulating red or yellow band of ten or twelve inches in breadth, surrounding the lodge at half its height; on others, rude figures of horses, buf-

faloe or deer were painted; others again with attempts at the human face, in a circle, as the moon
is sometimes painted; these were not less than
four feet in diameter. I judged there were not
fewer than eighty lodges. I did not remain long on
the summit of the bluffs, as I soon perceived, from
the heaps of earth, some of these recent, that it
was the burial ground, and I knew the veneration
they have for the graves of their ancestors. I proceeded along the bluffs, and was very successful in
my researches, but had not been long employed,
when I saw an old Indian galloping towards me;
he came up and shook hands with me, and pointing to the plants I had collected, said, " Bon
pour manger?" to which I replied, " Ne pas bon ;"
he then said, " Bon pour medicine ?" I replied
" Oui." He again shook hands, and rode away,
leaving me somewhat surprised at being addressed in
French by an Indian. On my return through the
village, I was stopped by a group of squaws, who
invited me *very kindly* into their lodges, calling
me Wakendaga, or as it is pronounced, We-ken-
da-ga, (Physician) I declined to accept their invitation, shewing them that the sun was near setting,
and that it would be night before I could reach
the boats; they then invited me to stay all night,
this also I declined, but suffered them to examine
my plants, for all which I found they had names.
On my way to the boats, I met a number of In-

dians returning to the village, all of whom shook hands with me. Two of them informed me that they had seen me at St. Louis, and at the same time gave me satisfactory proofs of it.* I did not reach the boats until it was dark.

13th.—In the forenoon of this day, Mr. Hunt was waited upon by two chiefs, who were contending for the sanction of the government of the United States, to determine their claim to kingly power. Mr. Hunt declined interfering, not being vested with the powers to act. The names of these two chiefs were the Big Elk and the White Cow, the former of whom ultimately succeeded, and has since signalized himself by a fine specimen of Indian elo-

---

* The Indians are remarkable for strength of memory in this particular. They will remember a man whom they have only transiently seen, for a great number of years, and perhaps never during their lives forget him. I had no recollection of these Indians, but they pointed down the river to St. Louis, afterwards they took up the corner of their buffalo robe, held it before their faces, and turned it over as a man does a newspaper in reading it. This action will be explained by relating that I frequented the printing-office of Mr. Joseph Charless, when at St. Louis, to read the papers from the United States, when it often happened that the Indians at that place on business came into the office and sat down. Mr. Charless, out of pleasantry, would hand to each a newspaper, and out of respect for the custom of the whites, they examined it with as much attention as if they could read, turning it over at the same time that they saw me turn that with which I was engaged.

quence, at the funeral of a Sioux chief, in the Missouri territory.* The Maha's seem very friendly to the whites, and cultivate corn, beans, melons, squashes, and a small species of tobacco, (*Nicotiana rustica.*) In 1802 they were visited by the small-pox, which made dreadful havoc, and destroyed at least two thirds of the whole nation. At present they muster nearly two hundred warriors, and from the great number of children, I judge that they are again increasing. In stature they are much inferior to the Osages, although I noticed several, whom I thought would reach to six feet. Their hunting ground is from their village to *L'Eau qui Court,* and along that river.

14th.—This day three Sioux Indians arrived, of the Yankton Ahna tribe, who reported that several nations of the Sioux were assembling higher up the river, with an intention to oppose our progress. This news was concealed as much as possible from the *Voyageurs,* and we prepared for our departure on the following morning.

15th.—We embarked early and passed Floyd's Bluffs, so named from a person of the name of Floyd, (one of Messrs. Lewis and Clark's party) having been buried there. In the course of this day, I was in-

* See Appendix, No. II.

formed by Mr. M'Kenzie, that in the night of the 7th instant, during our journey to the Ottoes, eleven Sioux Indians, who *had given or devoted their clothes to the medicine,** ran into the camp with their tomahawks in their hands, and were instantly surrounded and taken prisoners. The leader, finding the party on their guard, and much stronger probably than he expected, immediately cried out to his followers in their language, " My children, do not hurt the white people." As the party were fully apprized of the murderous intentions of these miscreants, the general voice was for putting them to death, but Mr. Hunt would not consent to it, and ordered that they should be conveyed over the river in one of the boats, at the same time informing them, that if they were again caught by the party, every man should be sacrificed. From a coincidence of time and circumstances, it appeared almost certain that it was this party that had crossed the Missouri, near the mouth of the river Platte, in the canoe of which we saw the skeleton on the 28th of April; and that

---

* When a party on a war excursion are entirely foiled in their object, a dread of the scoffs which may be expected from their tribe, renders them furious ; and it often happens in such cases, that they throw away their clothes, or devote them to the Great Spirit, with an intention to do some desperate act. Any white man, or any party of whites whom they meet, and can overcome, is almost certain to be sacrificed in this case.

it was also this party that was discovered by Rogers hovering about the Otto village, as the Sioux are at war with the Ottoes; it therefore appeared that Mr. Crooks and myself had run more risk than we were sensible of at the time.

16th, 17th, and 18th.—We had a fair wind, and made considerable progress up the river; few opportunities were therefore afforded for walking. I regretted this circumstance, as the bluffs had a very interesting appearance. During a short excursion, I was enabled to ascertain that the lower part of the bluffs were impregnated with sulphur, mixed with sulphate of iron and selenite crystals.

19th.—About nine o'clock we observed three buffaloe cows and a calf swimming across the river. Two of them and the calf were killed, but we found them to be so poor that we only preserved the calf.

20th.—We were stopped all day by a strong head wind. I availed myself of this circumstance, and was very successful in my researches. We found that the river was rising rapidly; it rose during this day more than three feet: we therefore concluded that this was the commencement of the annual flood of the Missouri, occasioned by the melting of the snow on the rocky mountains.

21st.—The river continued to rise, and the current to increase in rapidity: the navigation was therefore rendered very difficult. I walked the greatest part of the day, chiefly on the bluffs, and found the summits for the most part covered with gravel, containing tumblers of feltspar, granite, and some porphyry.

22nd.—In the morning our hunters killed three buffaloes and two elks on an island, and as we were now arriving at the country of our enemies, the Sioux; it was determined that they should in a great measure confine themselves to the islands, in their search for game. We dined at the commencement of a beautiful prairie ; afterwards I went to the bluffs, and proceeded along them till near evening. On regaining the bank of the river, I walked down to meet the boats, but did not find them until a considerable time after it was dark, as they had stopped early in the afternoon, having met with a canoe, in which were two hunters of the names of Jones and Carson, who had been two years near the head of the Missouri. These men agreed to join the party, and were considered as a valuable acquisition, any accession of strength being now desirable. This day, for the first time, I was much annoyed by the abundance of the prickly pear. Against the thorns of this plant I found that

mockasons are but a slight defence. I observed
two species, *Cactus opuntia* and *Mamillaris*.

23rd.—When on the bluffs yesterday, I observed
in the river an extensive bend, and determined to
travel across the neck. I therefore did not embark
with the boats, but filled my shot pouch with
parched corn, and set out, but not without being
reminded by Mr. Hunt that we were now in an
enemy's country. In about two hours I had entirely passed the range of hills forming the boundary of the Missouri; and as I had before experienced, I found the soil and face of the conntry to
improve very much as we proceed from the river.
The hills here are only gentle swellings, and, together with the intervening vallies, were covered with
the most beautiful verdure. At a small distance
from my route I noticed a space, of several acres
in extent, of a more vivid green than the surrounding prairie, and on my nearer approach it had the
appearance of a rabbit burrow. From the previous
descriptions given by the hunters, I immediately
conceived it to be, what it proved, a colony of the
prairie dog.* The little animals had taken the
alarm before I reached their settlement, and were
sitting singly on the small hillocks of earth at the

---

* A species of *sciurus*, or squirrel, not described in the Syst.
Natura.

mouth of their holes. They were very clamourous, uttering a cry which has some resemblance to a shrill barking. I shot at several, but at the instant of the flash, they darted with surprising quickness into their holes, before the shot could reach them. I soon found the impossibility of procuring one with shot only, as unless they are instantaneously killed, they are certain to get into their holes, from the edges of which they never wander if a man is in sight. I continued to travel through this charming country till near the middle of the afternoon, when I again came to the bluffs of the Missouri, where, amongst a number of new plants, I found a fine species of *Ribes*, or currant. As it was now time to look for the boats, I went to the river, and proceeded down the bank, in the expectation of meeting them. I had probably travelled about two miles, when suddenly I felt a hand laid upon my shoulder, and turning round, saw a naked Indian with a bow bent in his hand, and the arrow pointed towards me. As I had no expectation of meeting any Indians excepting the Sioux, and as with them the idea of danger was associated, I took my gun from my shoulder, and by a kind of spontaneous movement put my hand towards the lock, when I perceived the Indian drew his bow still farther. I now found myself completely in his power; but recollecting that if an enemy, he would have shot me before I saw him, I held out my hand, which he took, and afterwards laid his hand on my breast, and in the Osage language said, " *Moi-he ton-ga de-ah,*" literally in English, " Big Knife you?"* which I luckily understood, and answered, " *Hoya,*" (yes) and laying my hand on his breast, said, " *No-do-wessie de-ah,*" (Sioux you.) He replied, " *Honkoska ponca wé ah,*" (no, poncar me.) He then pointed up the river, and I saw two other Indians running towards us, and not more than fifty yards distant. They soon came up, and all the three laid hold of me, pointing over the bluffs, and making signs that I should go with them. I resisted, and pushed off their hands. As the river had overflowed where we stood, I pointed to a sand-hill a small distance from us, to which we went and sat down. I amused them with my pocket compass for some time, when they again seized me, and I still resisted, and took out a small microscope. This amused them for some time longer, when on a sudden one of them leaped up and gave the war whoop. I laid hold of my gun, with an intention to defend myself, but was instantly relieved from apprehension by his pointing down the river, and I perceived the mast of one of the boats appear over the willows. The Indians seemed very much inclined to run away, but I invited them to accompany me to

---

* The Americans are called " the Big Knives" by the Indians of the Missouri.

the boats, and shewed them by signs that I would give them something to drink, which they complied with, but soon after disappeared. We travelled very late this evening, and encamped above the mouth of a small creek. It appeared that the three Indians went to inform their nation, as in the morning a number of them came to our camp, and also a white man, with a letter to Mr. Hunt from Mr. Lisa, one of the Missouri Fur Company, for whom he was agent. Mr. Lisa had arrived at the Mahas some days after we left, and had dispatched this man by land. It appeared he had been apprized of the hostile intentions of the Sioux, and the purport of the letter was to prevail on Mr. Hunt to wait for him, that they might, for mutual safety, travel together on that part of the river which those blood thirsty savages frequent. It was judged expedient to trade with the Indians for some jerked buffalo meat, and more than 1000 lbs. was obtained for as much tobacco as cost two dollars. About noon we set out, and at the distance of a league passed the mouth of the river called L'Eau qui Court, or Rapid River.

25th.—It was discovered early this morning, that two men who had engaged at the Mahas, and had received equipments to a considerable value, had deserted in the night. It was known that one of them could not swim, and we had passed a large creek about a league below, therefore the party went in pursuit, but without success.

26th.—Whilst at breakfast in a beautiful part of the river, we observed two canoes descending on the opposite side. In one, by the help of our glasses, we ascertained there were two white men, and in the other only one. A gun was discharged, when they discovered us, and crossed over. We found them to be three men belonging to Kentucky, whose names were Robinson, Hauberk, and Reesoner. They had been several years hunting on and beyond the Rocky Mountains, until they *imagined* they were tired of the hunting life; and having families and good plantations in Kentucky, were returning to them; but on seeing us, families, plantations, and all vanished; they agreed to join us, and turned their canoes adrift. We were glad of this addition to our number, as the Poncars had confirmed all that we had heard respecting the hostile disposition of the Nodowessies, or Sioux, towards us, with the additional information, that five nations or tribes had already assembled, with a determination to cut us off. Robinson was sixty-six years of age, and was one of the first settlers in Kentucky. He had been in several engagements with the Indians there, who really made it to the first settlers, what its name imports, " The Bloody Ground." In one of these engagements he had been scalped, and was obliged to wear a handkerchief on his head to protect the part. As the wind was fair, we this day made considerable progress, and had many fine views of the bluffs, along which, from the L'Eau qui Court, we had observed excellent roads, made by the buffaloes. These roads I had frequent opportunities of examining, and am of opinion that no engineer could have laid them out more judiciously.

27th.—The weather continued fine, as it had been for the last fortnight, and was delightful. For some days past it had been very warm, and the carcasses of drowned buffaloes on the islands and shores of the river became extremely offensive. We had a fine breeze from the S.E. and made all the sail the extreme cowardice of our Canadians would permit us, in order to reach Little Cedar Island,* as it was intended that we should stop there to procure new masts, some of our old ones being defective. Late in the evening we accomplished our purpose, to the joy of our voyageurs, who had frequently in the course of the day, when the boats heeled, cried out in agony, " *O mon Dieu! abattez le voile.*" As we had now in our party five men who had traversed the Rocky Mountains in various directions, the best possible route in which to cross

* 1075 miles from the mouth of the Missouri.

them became a subject of anxious enquiry. They all agreed that the route followed by Lewis and Clark was very far from being the best, and that to the southward, where the head waters of the Platte and Roche Jaune rivers rise, they had discovered a route far less difficult. This information induced Mr. Hunt to change his plan, which had originally been to ascend the Missouri to the Roche Jaune river, 1880 miles from the mouth, and at that place he purposed to commence his journey by land. It was now concluded that it would be more advise-able to abandon the Missouri at the Aricara Town, 450 miles lower down the river.

28th.—We arose at day-break, and the men soon found trees suitable for masts. Whilst they were preparing, I employed myself in examining this delightful spot. The island is about three quarters of a mile in length, and 500 yards in width. The middle part is covered with the finest cedar, round which is a border from 60 to 80 yards in width, in which were innumerable clumps of rose and cur-rant bushes, mixed with grape vines, all in flower, and all extremely fragrant. The currant is a new and elegant species, and is described by Pursh* as

---

* This man has been suffered to examine the collection of specimens which I sent to Liverpool, and to describe almost the whole, thereby depriving me both of the credit and profit of what was justly due to me.

Ribes aureum. ·Betwixt the clumps and amongst the cedars the buffaloes, elks, and antelopes had made paths, which were covered with grass and flowers. I have never seen a place, however embellished by art, equal to this in beauty. `In a few hours the masts were completed, and we proceeded on our voyage with a fine breeze in our favour. Since our departure from L'Eau qui Court, I had noticed that the bluffs had gradually continued to change in appearance. The quantity of alluvion on the border of the river had decreased as we proceeded, and had now entirely vanished. The bluffs continue in a regular declivity from their summits to the edge of the river, ·and the narrowness of the valley indicates a country formed of such hard materials as to oppose considerable resistance to the abrasion of the river. On these bluffs, and at about half the distance from the summit to the river, I began to notice a number of places of a deep brown colour, apparently divested of vegetation. They occurred on both sides of the river, with an exact correspondence in altitude and breadth, and exhibited the appearance of two interrupted lines running as far as the bluffs could be seen. As we were now in an enemy's country, it was with reluctance Mr. Hunt suffered me to land a little before dinner, when I proceeded to examine one of these spots. I found it almost entirely covered with iron ore, of that species called by Kirwan *compact iron stone ;* in Waller Syst. 2, p. 144, *Hæmatitis solidus.* I found its specific gravity to be 3.482. The oxidation of the ore had so changed the earth, that it resembled Spanish brown, and nothing grew on it but a few scattered shrubs of a species of *Artemisia,* apparently a non-descript. I hastened to the boats, and we kept our sails up the rest of the day, the bodies of ore becoming longer and more frequent as we proceeded. We travelled eighteen miles, and encamped one hour after sunset.

29th.—Some arrangements being necessary, the boats did not set out so early as usual, and daylight opened to our view one of the most interesting prospects I have ever seen. We had encamped at the commencement of a stretch of the river, about fifteen miles in length, as we judged, and nearly in a right line. The bluffs on both sides formed, as before, a gentle slope to the river, and not a single tree was visible. The body of iron ore had now become continuous on both sides of the river, and exhibited the appearance of two dark brown stripes, about 100 yards in breadth and fifteen miles long. The exact conformity of the two lines, and the contrast of colour produced by the vivid green which bounded them, formed a coup d'oeil which I have never seen paralelled. I lamented much that the wind was fair, but availed myself of the short delay, and hastened up the bluff to the vein of ore, where, although the soil was so strongly impregnated with iron as to resemble rust, I observed a number of large white flowers on the ground, belonging to a new species of *œnothera*, having neither stem or scape, the flower sitting immediately on the root. On a signal being given from the boats, I was obliged to return, and had no farther opportunity to examine this enormous body of ore, without doubt sufficient to supply the whole of North America with iron for thousands of years; and when we combine in the same view the abundance of coal on the Missouri, it warrants a presumption that in some future age it will become an object of vast national importance.

30th.—We set out this morning with a favourable wind, which continued during the whole of the day; and the course of the river being less crooked than usual, we made thirty miles, and slept on an island.

31st.—Before breakfast this morning we discovered two Indians on a bluff on the north east side of the river, we stopped opposite to them to breakfast, during which they frequently harangued us in a loud tone of voice. After we had breakfasted, Mr. Hunt went over the river to speak to them, and took with him Dorion, the interpreter. We noticed, that when he landed, one of the Indians went away, and for a short time disappeared from our sight, but immediately reappeared on horseback, and went at full speed over the bluffs. Mr. Hunt informed us on his return, that these Indians belonged to the Sioux nations ; that three tribes were encamped about a league from us, and had 280 lodges. They were the Yangtons Ahnah, the Tetons Bois Brulé, and the Tetons Min-na-kine-azzo. The Indian informed Mr. Hunt that they had been waiting for us eleven days, with a decided intention of opposing our progress, as they would suffer no one to trade with the Ricaras, Mandans, and Minaterees, being at war with those nations. It is usual to reckon two warriors to each lodge, we therefore found that we had to oppose near six hundred savages, with the character of whom we were well acquainted ;* and it had also

---

* In the statistical account of the Missouri, by Lewis, read before Congress in February, 1806, the character of these Indians is thus described :—" These are the vilest miscreants of the savage race, and must ever remain the pirates of the Missouri, until such measures are pursued by our government as will make them feel a dependence on its will for their supply of merchandize. Unless these people are reduced to order by coercive measures, I am ready to pronounce that the citizens of the United States can never enjoy but partially the advantages which the Missouri presents. Relying on a regular supply of merchandize through the channel of the river St. Peter's, they view with contempt the merchants of the Missouri, whom they never fail to plunder when in their power. Persuasion or advice with them

been stated by the Indian that they were in daily
expectation of being joined by two other tribes,
Tetons Okandandas and Tetons Sahone. We proceeded up the river, and passed along an island,
which, for about half an hour, intercepted our
view of the north east side of the river. On
reaching the upper point we had a view of the
bluffs, and saw the Indians pouring down in great
numbers, some on horseback, and others on foot.
They soon took possession of a point a little above
us, and ranged themselves along the bank of the
river. By the help of our glasses, we could perceive that they were all armed and painted for war.
Their arms consisted chiefly of bows and arrows,
but a few had short carbines : they were also provided with round shields. We had an ample sufficiency of arms for the whole party, which now
consisted of sixty men; and besides our small
arms, we had a swivel, and two howitzers. Any

---

is viewed as supplication, and only tends to inspire them with
contempt for those who offer either. The tameness with which
the traders of the Missouri have heretofore submitted to their
rapacity, has tended not a little to inspire them with a poor opinion of the white persons who visit them through that channel.
A prevalent idea, and one which they make the rule of their conduct, is, that the more harshly they behave towards the traders,
the greater the quantity of merchandize they will bring them,
and that they will obtain the articles they wish on better terms.
They have endeavoured to inspire the Aricaras with similar sen-
timents, but happily without effect.

attempt to avoid the Indians would have been abortive, inasmuch as a boat, in ascending the Missouri, can only effect it by going along the edges of the river, it being wholly impossible to stem the middle current; and as the banks are in many places high and perpendicular, we must inevitably be in their power frequently, as they might several times in the course of a day shower a volley of arrows upon us, and retire unseen. Our alternative, therefore, was, as we supposed, either to fight them or return. The former was immediately decided on, and we landed nearly opposite to the main body. Our first care was to put all the arms in complete order: afterwards the swivel and the howitzers were loaded with powder only, and fired to impress them with an idea that we were well prepared. They were then heavily loaded, and with as many bullets as it was supposed they would bear, after which we crossed the river. When we arrived within about one hundred yards of them, the boats were stationed, and all seized their arms. The Indians now seemed to be in confusion, and when we rose up to fire, they spread their buffaloe robes before them, and moved them from side to side. Our interpreter called out, and desired us not to fire, as the action indicated, on their part, a wish to avoid an engagement, and to come to a parley. We accordingly desisted, and saw about fourteen

of the chiefs separate themselves from the crowd
who were on the summit of the bank, and descend
to the edge of the river, where they sat down on
the sand, forming themselves into a portion of a
circle, in the centre of which we could see preparations making to kindle a fire, evidently with a
design to smoke the calumet with us, and signs
were made, inviting us to land. Mr. Hunt requested that Messrs. Crooks, M'Kenzie, Miller, and
M'Clellan would attend him in his boat, and I accompanied Mr. M'Kenzie. The object was to consider
whether it was advisable to place so much confidence
in so ferocious and faithless a set, as to accept the
invitation. It did not require much deliberation,
as we found ourselves under the necessity of either
fighting or treating with them, it was therefore
determined to hazard the experiment of going
ashore. The party who remained in the boats
were ordered to continue in readiness to fire on the
Indians instantly, in case of treachery, and Messrs.
Hunt, M'Kenzie, Crooks, Miller, and M'Clellan,
with the interpreter and myself, went ashore.
We found the chiefs sitting where they had first
placed themselves, as motionless as statues; and
without any hesitation or delay, we sat down on
the sand, in such a manner as to complete the circle. When we were all seated, the pipe was
brought by an Indian, who seemed to act as priest
on this occasion; he stepped within the circle, and

lighted the pipe. The head was made of a red stone, known by mineralogists under the term of *killas,* and is often found to accompany copper ore ; it is procured on the river St. Peters, one of the principal branches of the Mississippi. The stem of the pipe was at least six feet in length, and highly decorated with tufts of horse hair, dyed red. After the pipe was lighted, he held it up towards the sun, and afterwards pointed it towards the sky, in different directions. He then handed it to the great chief, who smoked a few whiffs, and taking the head of the pipe in his hand, commenced by applying the other end to the lips of Mr. Hunt, and afterwards did the same to every one in the circle. When this ceremony was ended, Mr. Hunt rose, and made a speech in French, translated as he proceeded into the Sioux language by Dorion. The purport of the speech was to state, that the object of our voyage up the Missouri was not to trade; that several of our brothers had gone to the great salt lake in the west, whom we had not seen for eleven moons. That we had come from the great salt lake in the east, on our way to see our brothers, for whom we had been *crying* ever since they left us; and our lives were now become so miserable for the want of our brothers, that we would rather die than not go to them, and would kill every man that should oppose our passage. That we had heard of their design to prevent our passage up the river, but we did not wish to believe it, as we were determined to persist, and were, as they might see, well prepared to effect our purpose; but as a proof of our pacific intentions, we had brought them a present of tobacco and corn. About fifteen carottes of tobacco, and as many bags of corn, were now brought from the boat, and laid in a heap near the great chief, who then rose and commenced a speech, which was repeated in French by Dorion. He commenced by stating that they were at war with the Ricaras, Mandans, and Gros Ventres or Minaterees, and the injury it would be to them if these nations were furnished with arms and amunition; but as they found we were only going to our brothers, they would not attempt to stop us. That he also had brothers, at a great distance northward, whom he had not seen for a great many moons, and for whom he also had been *crying*. He professed himself satisfied with our present, and advised us to encamp on the other side of the river, for fear his *young men* should be troublesome. When the speech was ended, we all rose, shook hands, and returned to the boats. During this conference, I had an opportunity of noticing these Indians, a great number of whom were assembled on the bank above us, and observed that they are in stature considerably below the Osages Mahas, and Poncars, and much less robust. They

are also much more deficient in clothing and ornaments, a considerable number being entirely naked,
but all armed. Several of our party were acquainted with these tribes, and represent them much as
described by Lewis. Although the squaws are
very ill treated by all Indians, it is said these treat
them much worse than any other tribe, whence it
follows that the mothers frequently destroy their
female children, alleging as a reason, that it is better they should die than live to lead a life so miserable as that to which they are doomed. Amongst
the Sioux women also it is said suicide is not un-
frequent, and the mode which they adopt to put
an end to their existence, is by hanging themselves.
They are of opinion that suicide is displeasing to
the *Father of Life*, and believe will be punished in
the *land of spirits* by the ghost being doomed for
ever to drag the tree on which they hang themselves : for this reason they always suspend themselves to as small a tree as can possibly sustain their
weight. In the course of the afternoon we met a
chief who belonged to a party of Teton Okandandas,
consisting, as he said, of 30 lodges. He asked for
a passage in the boats during the rest of the day.
It was granted to him, and he remained with us
during the night.

June 1.—This morning the old chief was conveyed over the river, and landed on the opposite

side, as he said he expected to meet his people, but we did not see him again. In the afternoon we entered upon the Great Bend, or, as the French call it, the Grand Detour, and encamped about five miles above the lower entrance. This bend is said to be twenty-one miles in circuit by the course of the river, and only 1900 yards across the neck.

2nd.—In the morning early we discovered two Indians standing on the bluffs before us, who immediately after discovering us, spread their buffalo robes in token of being amicably inclined towards us. We crossed over the river, and when we approached them, they spread out their arms in a horizontal position. This action, I was informed, was an appeal to our clemency. When we landed they shewed evident symptoms of alarm. This was soon accounted for by Messrs. Crooks, M'Clellan, and Miller, who informed us that they knew these fellows, and that they were chiefs of the Sahonies and Okanandans, who the year preceding had behaved extremely ill, by plundering and otherwise maltreating them, in such a manner as to render it necessary for their safety to escape down the river in the night, and abandon the trade with the upper Indians for that year, which had been a great loss to them. They seemed very apprehensive that Mr. Crooks would now resent their conduct; but after we had smoked with them they became more tranquil. During the smoking Mr. Hunt asked them why they killed white men, as he heard that they had killed three during the last summer? They replied, because the white men kill us: that man (pointing to Carson) killed one of our brothers last summer. This was true. Carson, who was at that time amongst the Ricaras, fired across the Missouri at a war party of Sioux, and it was by a very extraordinary chance he killed one of them, as the river is fully half a mile in breadth, and in retaliation the Sioux killed three white men. I observed that, as before, in smoking the pipe they did not make use of tobacco, but the bark of *Cornus sanguinea*, or red dog wood, mixed with the leaves of *Rhus glabra*, or smooth sumach. This mixture they call kinnikineck. After we had smoked, they spoke of the poverty of their tribes, and ended by saying they expected a present. A few carottes of tobacco and bags of corn were laid at their feet, and they appeared satisfied. As these were the last of the Sioux tribes we expected to meet, I now determined to walk all day, and was much pleased that the restraint imposed on me by the proximity of these vagabonds was now removed. I therefore proceeded up the bluffs nearly abreast of the boats. In about a quarter of an hour afterwards two other Indians rode hastily past me, and overtook the boats. I observed that they had a short conference with Mr. Hunt, when they turned their horses about, and again rode past me, seemingly in a rage. Mr. Hunt called to me, and requested that I would come on board instantly, and I was informed by him that these fellows were also chiefs, and had seen our presents, with which they were much dissatisfied, and in consequence had followed the boats to extort more. In reply to their insolent demands, Mr. Hunt informed them that " he had given all he intended to give, and would give no more," adding, " that he was much displeased by their importunity, and if they or any of their nation again followed us with similar demands, he would consider them as enemies, and treat them as such." As we were not exactly acquainted with the strength of these two tribes, and expected that, in consequence of the disappointment in their rapacious demands, they would attack us, it was arranged that the large boat should ascend on the N.E. side of the river, and the three small boats on the S.W. as the bluffs on either side of the river can be seen much better from the opposite side ; and it was agreed that the signal on seeing Indians should be two shots fired in quick succession. As we had not much apprehension of being attacked on the S.W. side, I went ashore after dinner, and continued along the river nearly on a line with the boats, and about four o'clock heard the signal given of Indians being seen. I instantly ran towards the boats, and arrived as they were preparing to quit the shore to aid Mr. Hunt and his party in the large boat, apparently then in the most imminent danger. They had passed betwixt a large sand bar and the shore, and it was evident to us that at that juncture they had found the water too shallow at the upper end, and were under the necessity of turning back. The sand bar prevented the possibility of putting out into the river, and we saw with horror that at least 100 Indians had arrived on the bank at the lower end of the bar: we could also perceive that they were a war party, as they were painted with black and white stripes, and all had shields.* As we had every reason to conclude that these were the Teton Okandandas and the Teton Sahonies, our anxiety for the safety of Mr. Hunt and the party in the large boat was indescribable when we saw large bodies of the Indians every moment arrive at the point near which he must unavoidably pass, before we could possibly give him any assistance: but our anxiety was changed to surprise on seeing the boat pass within a short distance of them unmolested; soon after

---

* It may be observed here, that all the Indians who inhabit the prairie use shields in war; but to those who inhabit a woody region they are wholly unknown, as in action, excepting in close fight, each man conceals himself behind a tree. The shields made use of are circular, and near thirty inches in diameter. They are covered with three or four folds of buffalo skin, dried hard in the sun, and are proof against arrows, but not a bullet.

which the Indians ran along the bank to the upper
end of the sand bar, threw down their arms, their
shields, and their buffalo robes, and plunged into
the river in crowds to meet us; and before we
could reach the sand bar, they were round our
boats, holding up their hands in such numbers, that
it became tiresome to shake hands with so many.
We now found that this was a war party, consisting
of Aricaras, Mandans, and Minetarees, or Gros
Ventres, who were come against the Sioux, and
having discovered us, had determined for the present to abandon the enterprise, expecting that on
our arrival at the Aricara Town they would obtain
a supply of fire arms and ammunition, which would
give them a superiority over their enemies. During the ceremony of shaking hands we were joined
by the large boat, and it was determined that we
should encamp at the first convenient place. We
soon found one that was suitable, and the Indians
fixed their camp about one hundred yards from
ours. I now ascertained that the party consisted
of near 300 warriors. As we had plenty of provisions, a supply was given to the Indians, who prepared their supper, after which the chiefs and principal warriors came to our tents. In Mr. M'Kenzie's tent there were seven, none of whom appeared
to me to be lower than five feet ten inches; some
more than six feet. Most of them had very good
countenances, differing from the heavy face of the

Osage, or the keen visage of the Sioux. One of
them had an aquiline nose, and had a scarified line
running along each arm, and meeting on his sto-
mach. I enquired of our interpreter for what purpose he had done it? He said it was to show his
grief for the death of his father. Whilst I was
endeavouring to converse with him, an Indian boy
came into the tent, and handed water round to the
chiefs in a gourd shell tied to the end of a stick.
He spoke to the boy, who went out, but soon returned with a new pair of ornamented mockasons,
and handed them to the warrior, who it then appeared had observed that mine were dirty and far
worn, as he took them off my feet, and put on the
new pair, tying them himself. I observed that he
had a short carbine and a powder flask. I begged
to look at the latter, and finding it only contained
a very small quantity of powder, I immediately filled it from my own flask. He was greatly pleased
with the acquisition of so much powder, and informed me that he was a Ricara, and should meet
me at their town, where we should be brothers.
We were interrupted by one of the chiefs crying
" How," signifying amongst the Indians " Come
on," or " let us begin." This occasioned silence,
and he began to strike on one hand with a war club
which he held in the other. It had a globular
head, on one side of which was fixed the blade of
a knife, five or six inches in length. The head

was hollow, and contained small bits of metal, which made a jingling noise as he struck in quick time. The singing now commenced, and continued at intervals until past midnight. The song is very rude, and it does not appear that they are capable of combining the expression of ideas with music, the whole of their singing consisting in the repetition of the word *ha* six or seven times in one tone, after which they rose or fell a third, fourth, or fifth, and the same in quick time. I observed that their voices were in perfect unison, and although, according to our ideas of music, there was neither harmony nor melody, yet the effect was pleasing, as there was evidently system, all the changes of tone being as exactly conformable in point of time as if only one voice had been heard. Whenever their performance ceased the termination was extremely abrupt, by pronouncing the word *how* in a quick and elevated tone.

On the morning of the 3d, the chiefs declared to Mr. Hunt their intention of immediately returning to their nation, and that they expected to arrive in three days, although they had been sixteen days in coming out. They also demanded some arms and ammunition. This demand, conformable to the custom of war parties, had been foreseen, but was not complied with; as Mr. Hunt informed them, that when we arrived at their nation, we should furnish abundance. After we had left them, the chief overtook us on horseback, and said that his people were not satisfied to go home without some proof of their having seen the white men. Mr. Hunt could not now resist, and gave him a cask of powder, a bag of balls, and three dozen of knives, with which he was much pleased. Whilst the articles were delivering to him, an Indian came running up, and informed us that there was a boat in sight, coming up the river. We immediately concluded that it was the boat belonging to Manuel Lisa, and after proceeding five or six miles, we waited for it. I was much pleased, on the boat's joining us, to find that Mr. Henry Brackenridge was along with Mr. Lisa; I became acquainted with him at St. Louis, and found him a very amiable and interesting young man. Mr. Lisa had made the greatest possible exertions to overtake us, being well apprised of the hostile disposition of the Sioux. He had met a boat, which, it appeared, had passed us in the night, and the people informed him that they had been fired upon by the Indians. As the conjunct party now consisted of ninety men, and we were approaching the nations who were at war with the Sioux, our fears had almost subsided; and for myself, I was much gratified on finding the restraints removed which had so long circumscribed my motions. In the early part of this day the wind was fair, but after we had proceeded some miles, it changed to north east, and blew so strong, that we could not stem the torrent against it, and our difficulties were increased by the rising of the river. I went to the bluffs, which in this part are of considerable elevation, but rise in a gentle slope from the river; near the summit is a stratum of deep brown-coloured earth, from two to three hundred feet in breadth, on the declivity of the hill. This earth appears mostly to consist of decomposed iron ore, and is evidently a continuation of that seen near Little Cedar Island, although distant from it near 100 miles in a right line. I observed, that uniformly the flat tops of the hills were nearly covered with masses of stone, chiefly *Breccia*. There was something so singularly constant in this appearance, that I was tempted to attend to a particular examination, and became convinced that these groupes of stone were the *passive* cause of the hills. If the group was of an oblong form, the hill was a *ridge;* it was nearly circular, the hill was a *cone.* It would be difficult to describe the sensations occasioned by a view at once of these hillls, and the valley of the Missouri. The mind is irresitsibly impressed with the belief that the whole surface of the surrounding country was once *at least* on a level with the tops of these hills; and that all below has been carried away by the erosion of water, from which it has been protected in the parts where these stones were collected.* I remarked this day, that the wolves appeared to be more numerous and more daring than in any former part of our voyage. Within the last week, we had frequently seen a few in the course of each day, but now, some of them were almost constantly in sight, and so fearless, as frequently to stand at no great distance to gaze. For the present, they were protected by their worthlessness, their skins being out of season. It appears that in a natural state, the wolf is a *diurnal* animal; but in the neighbourhood of condensed and stationary population its habits change, and it becomes *nocturnal*.† On my route this day I saw numerous colonies of the prairie dog; and from the frequency of the occurrence, I noticed that my approach to their burrows was announced by the screams of a species of corlieu. I shot one, and ascertained it to be a variety of *Scolopax arquata;* and perceived, after I noticed the fact, that the alarm was invariably given. On my return to the boats, I found that some of the leaders of our party were

---

* An enquiry into the length of time which it has required to produce this effect, might be a matter of great interest to the *Chinese* philosophers.

† During the Autumn, whilst the Indians are employed in killing game for their Winter's stock, the wolves associate in flocks, and follow them at a distance to feed on the refuse of the carcases; and will often sit within view, waiting until the Indians have taken what they chuse, and abandoned the rest.

extremely apprehensive of treachery on the part of Mr. Lisa, whom they suspected had an intention of quitting us shortly, being now no longer in fear of the Sioux, with an intention of doing us an injury with the Aricaras. Independant of this feeling, it had required all the address and influence of Mr. Hunt to prevent Mr. M'Clellan or Mr. Crooks from calling him to account for instigating the Sioux to treat them ill the preceding year. Besides, it was believed by all, that although apparently friendly, he was anxiously desirous that the expedition should fail. Lisa had twenty oars, and made much greater expedition than we had, it was evident, therefore, that he had it in his power to leave us, and it was determined to watch his conduct narrowly.

4th.—The boats did not make much way, and I walked chiefly on and beyond the bluffs, which I found of the same description as those observed yesterday, and on still farther examination, became more confirmed in my opinion regarding the origin of the hills. On the summit of one I found some fragments of bones in a petrified state, apparently belonging to the buffalo. I had for some time past noticed on the declivities circular spaces of about six or seven feet in diameter, wholly divested of every kind of vegetation, and covered with small gravel. The frequent occurrence of these this day attracted my more particular attention, and I found that they were caused by a large species of black ant, hundreds of which were running in every direction within the area with astonishing activity. On finding a large beetle, I put it in the centre of one of these areas, when it was instantly seized by those nearest to it. For a short time the ants were dragged along with ease ; but by some unknown and surprising faculty the intelligence was immediately spread throughout the whole space : they ran from every direction towards the centre, and in a few seconds the poor beetle became completely covered, and escape was impossible.

5th.—We had not proceeded more than four miles before a very heavy rain commenced, and we were compelled to stop and fix up the tents. I went as usual to the bluffs, and on my return to secure some interesting specimens of plants, found that Lisa had encamped about one hundred yards above us. After I had dried my clothes, I again visited the bluffs in company with Mr. Brackenridge. We discovered on the bank of a small creek the remains of an Indian encampment, which had apparently been occupied by a considerable number, and for some time, as there was a great quantity of bones spread on the ground, and the marks where the wigwams stood were numerous. We agreed that the situation was judiciously chosen to

prevent surprise. On ascending the hills, and looking over the summit, we observed near us a small
herd of buffaloes, consisting of two cows and three
bulls. We immediately drew back, and taking
advantage of a ravine, approached within thirty or
forty yards, and fired. We wounded one of the
cows, which Mr. Brackenridge pursued. Several
other herds of buffaloes were in view, and some
antelopes or cabri. I found the hills all capped
with stones, and was still more confirmed in my
opinion respecting their formation by observing
some large detached blocks, each lying on a small
pyramid of clay. After Mr. Brackenridge joined
me, we observed a large hare, *Lepus variabilis,* the
first I had noticed, and also a number of wolves in
several directions, and returning through an extensive colony of prairie dogs, we regained the
boats. Immediately on my return to our camp, a
circumstance happened that for some time threatened to produce tragical consequences. It appeared that during our absence Mr. Lisa had invited
Dorion, our interpreter, to his boat, where he had
given him some whiskey, and took that opportunity
of avowing his intention to take him away from
Mr. Hunt, in consequence of a debt due by Dorion to the Missouri Fur Company, for whom Lisa
was agent. Dorion had often spoken to us of this
debt, and in terms of great indignation at the manner in which it had been incurred, alleging that he

had been charged the most exorbitant prices for
articles had at Fort Mandan, and in particular ten
dollars per quart for whiskey.   Some harsh words
had therefore passed betwixt him and Lisa, and
he returned to our camp.   On the instant of my
arrival, Mr. Lisa came to borrow a *cordeau,* or
towing-line, from Mr. Hunt, and being perceived
by Dorion, he instantly sprung out of his tent, and
struck him.   Lisa flew into the most violent rage,
cried out, " *O mon Dieu! ou est mon couteau!*"
and ran precipitately to his boat.   As it was expected he would return armed, Dorion got a pair
of pistols, and took his ground, the party ranging
themselves in order to witness the event.   Soon
after, Mr. Lisa appeared without pistols; but it
was observed that he had his knife in his girdle.
As Dorion had disclosed what had passed in Lisa's
boat, Messrs. Crooks and M'Clellan were each
very eager to take up the quarrel, but were res-
trained by Mr. Hunt, until an expression from
Lisa, conveying an imputation upon himself, made
him equally desirous of fighting.   He told Lisa
that the matter should be settled by themselves,
and desired him to fetch his pistols.   I followed
Lisa to his boat, accompanied by Mr. Brackenridge, and we with difficulty prevented a meeting,
which, in the present temper of the parties, would
certainly have been a bloody one.

The river had risen considerably during the night, and we were now convinced that the floods we had before encountered, and which were of short duration, were only partial; and caused by the rising of the tributary streams, having their sources in the lower regions. The periodical flood is occasioned by the melting of the snows on the rocky mountains, and the plains at their feet. The boats ascended with difficulty, which gave opportunities for walking the whole of the day. In the early part, we passed the remains of an old Aricara village. The scite was indicated by an embankment, on which had been pallisadoes, as the remains were still visible. Within the area, the vestiges of the lodges were very apparent, and great quantities of bones, and fragments of earthenware were scattered in every part. The wolves are still numerous, and are mostly of a light grey colour, with a few black hairs intermixed on the hind part of the back: they are seen singly, and although not timid, show no disposition to attack. Happening to come on one this day suddenly and unperceived, I shot him. He was large, and appeared to be old, as his teeth were much worn. The country beyond the bluffs continues still very fine, but cut up in many places by deep ravines, occasioned by torrents during heavy rains. The sides of these ravines uniformly exhibited an under stratum of hard yellow clay, of an indeterminate depth.

7th.—Went out early on the S. W. side, with some of the hunters, and on reaching the summit of the bluffs, observed a range of high hills passing off to the westward, apparently to the distance of thirty or forty miles. These, I was informed, by the hunters, bounded the Chien or Chayenne river. Two buffaloe were killed, and one Cabri, or antelope. The hunter who killed the last assured me that he had allured it by putting a handkerchief at the end of his ramrod, and lying down, continued to wave it, whilst he remained concealed: the animal, it seems, after a long contest betwixt curiosity and fear, approached near enough to become a sacrifice to the former.

8th.—Since the affair of the 5th, our party has had no intercourse with that of Mr. Lisa, as he kept at a distance from us, and mostly on the opposite side of the river; this deprived me of the society of my friend Brackenridge. I regretted this circumstance, and purposed to have joined him this morning, but was prevented by our stopping to breakfast, on an island, on which our hunters killed two buffaloe and two elk. Of the former, we had, for some days past, seen a great number of herds, consisting of from fifty to a

H

hundred in each. On expressing my surprise, the hunters assured me, that so far from its being extraordinary, they had been in the expectation of seeing them in much greater numbers. Some of the hunters, who had been six or eight years about the head of the Missouri, said they had seen them during their annual migrations from north to south, in Autumn, and to the northward in Spring. They all agreed in stating, that at these times they assemble in vast herds, marching in regular order. Some asserted that they had been able to distinguish where the herds were beyond the bounds of the visible horizon, by the vapour which arose from their bodies. Others stated that they had seen herds extending many miles in length. It appeared also to be a well known fact among them, that in these periodical migrations, they are much less fearful of the hunter. I must observe of the hunters, that any accounts which I heard from them, and afterwards had an opportunity to prove, I found to be correct;* and when the great extent of

---

* During our voyage, I often associated with the hunters, to collect information from their united testimony, concerning the nature and habits of animals, with which no men are so well acquainted. This knowledge is absolutely necessary to them, that they may be able to circumvent or surprise those which are the objects of chase, and to avoid such as are dangerous; and likewise to prevent being surprised by them. They can imitate the cry or note of any animal found in the American Wilds, so

this plain, and its fertility in grass are considered, we cannot but admit that the number of animals it is capable of containing must be immense. In

---

exactly, as to deceive the animals themselves. I shall here state a few, of what I certainly believe to be, facts ; some I know to be so, and of others I have seen strong presumptive proofs. The opinion of the hunters, respecting the sagacity of the Beaver, goes much beyond the statements of any author whom I have read. They state that an old beaver, who has escaped from a trap, can scarcely ever be caught afterwards, as travelling in situations where traps are usually placed, he carries a stick in his mouth, with which he probes the sides of the river, that the stick may be caught in the trap, and thus saves himself.

They say also of this animal, that the young are educated by the old ones. It is well known that in constructing their dams, the first step the beaver takes, is to cut down a tree that shall fall across the stream intended to be dammed up. The hunters in the early part of our voyage informed me, that they had often found trees near the edge of a creek, in part cut through and abandoned, and always observed that those trees would not have fallen across the creek, and that by comparing the marks left by the teeth on those trees, with others, they found them much smaller ; and therefore not only concluded that they were made by young beavers, but that the old ones perceiving their error, had caused them to desist. They promised to shew me proofs of this, and during our voyage I saw several, and in no instance would the trees, thus abandoned, have fallen across the creek.

I have myself witnessed an instance of a doe, when pursued, although not many seconds out of sight, so effectually to hide her fawn, that we could not find it although assisted by a dog. I mentioned this fact to the hunters who assured me that no dog nor perhaps any beast of prey, can follow a fawn by the scent, and shewed me in a full grown deer, a gland and a tuft of red hair situated a little above the hind part of the fore foot which had a

the forenoon, we passed the mouth of Chayenne
river, where it is 400 yards in width. It is described by the hunters as being a very fine river,
and navigable for several hundred miles. We encamped this night in a beautiful grove, ornamented
with a number of rose and currant bushes, entwined with grape vines, now in bloom.

9th.—Mr. M'Clellan, with two of our men, and
three belonging to Lisa, were dispatched to the
Aricaras, to apprize them of our coming, and to
see how far it was practicable to procure horses for
the journey by land. Soon after we set out, we
saw a great number of buffaloe on both sides of
the river, over which several herds were swimming.
Notwithstanding all the efforts made by these poor
animals, the rapidity of the current brought numbers of them within a few yards of our boats, and
three were killed. We might have obtained a
great many more, but for once we did not kill *because* it was in our power to do so; but several
were killed from Lisa's boat. In the evening, Mr.
Lisa encamped a little above us, and we were informed by his party, that about sun-set they had
seen six Indians.

---

very strong smell of musk. This tuft they call the *scent*, and
believe that the route of the animal is betrayed by the effluvia
proceeding from it. This tuft is mercifully withheld until the
animal has acquired strength. What a benevolent arrangement!

10th.—A fine breeze sprang up early in the day, and we proceeded rapidly. About noon, Mr. M'Clellan and his party appeared on the bank of the river, having found that they could not reach the Aricara nation before the boats. About the middle of the afternoon, we met a canoe with three Indians. They had come from the Aricaras, where intelligence of our approach had been brought by the war party which met with us on the 1st. They had made a great parade with the presents which they received from us, and of the exploit which they had achieved in discovering the white men coming. They reported that the Mandans, who were of the party, had urged that they should attack Mr. Hunt's boat, when it was in the situation already described, which they, (the Aricaras) had prevented. They also stated, that the Minatarees, or Gros Ventres Indians had killed two white men, on the river above the Missouri Fur Company's fort. We encamped three miles above the mouth of the river *Cer-wer-cer-na*, after travelling thirty-five miles.

11th.—We hoped this day to arrive at the Aricaras, but did not derive so much benefit from the wind as we expected; and after passing the river *Ma-ra-pa*, we encamped about six miles below the town, near an island on which they were formerly settled.

12th.—During this night we had a severe thunder storm, and such torrents of rain, that our beds were completely wet. We set out early, and about half way to the town, we met a canoe with two chiefs, and an interpreter, who is a Frenchman, and has lived with this tribe more than twenty years: he married a squaw, and has several children. The chiefs were good looking men; one of them is called the head chief, or king, and is named by the French *Le Gauche*, being left-handed; the other is the war chief, and called the *Big Man*. The interpreter informed us that the chiefs had come to a resolution to oppose our farther progress up the river, unless a boat was left to trade with them. Mr. Hunt explained to the chiefs the object of his voyage, and that he would willingly trade for horses. About ten o'clock, we landed on the north side, opposite the town, or rather towns, as there are two distinct bands, and their villages are about eighty yards apart. Our first care was to spread out the beds and baggage to dry. Whilst the men were occupied in this business, the chief informed us, from the other side of the river, that he would be ready to meet us in council, when we should chuse to come over. As the river is here at least eight or nine hundred yards in breadth, it may appear surprising that he could make himself understood at so great a distance; but to those who have heard the In-

dian languages spoken, and who are acquainted with
the Indians, it will appear very credible. In
all the Indian languages which I have heard, every
syllable of the compound words is accented; as,
for instance, the primitive name of this nation,
Starrahe, they pronounce *Stăr-ră-hĕ.* In addition
to this construction of their languages, the Indians have remarkably loud voices. The leaders of
our two parties had not yet spoken to each other,
since the affair of the 5th; nor had any communication, except through the medium of Mr. Brackenridge or myself. It was evident that Lisa was
still suspected; and M'Clellan, in particular, carefully watched his motions, determined to shoot
him if he attempted to cross the river before us, to
attend the council of the Indians, contrary to what
had been previously agreed upon with Mr. Brackenridge on his behalf. Soon after noon, Mr. Hunt man-
ned the large boat, and with Messrs. M'Kenzie and
M'Clellan, went over the river: Lisa also attended in his barge. Mr. Brackenridge and myself
were of the party. On landing, amongst a crowd
of Indians, we were conducted to the council
lodge by some chiefs, who met us; where we sat
down on buffaloe skins prepared for us, and spread
on the ground. I noticed that this lodge was constructed in a manner similar to those already described, belonging to the Ottoes. An old Indian
lighted the pipe, and handed it to the chief; after

which he squatted himself on his hams, near the entrance of the lodge. Although there were nearly twenty present, I soon learned from Dorion, (near whom I had placed myself) that several of the chiefs were not yet assembled. After we had smoked for a short time, *Le Gauche,* the chief, spoke to the old Indian at the door, who went out of the lodge : he soon after appeared on the top, and was visible to us through the hole left for the smoke. What the chief dictated to him from within, he bawled out aloud, with the lungs of a Stentor. I understood that his object was to summon the chiefs to council, and it was promptly obeyed, as in ten minutes all were assembled. I now found that although we had smoked, the council pipe had not been yet lighted; this was now done by the same old Indian, who it seems was both priest and herald. *Le Gauche* made the customary appeal to the Great Spirit, by puffing the smoke in different directions towards heaven and earth; after which the pipe was applied to the lips of each assembled, the chief still holding it. He then opened the council by a short speech : in the first place, he spoke of their poverty, but said that they were very glad to see us, and would be still more glad to trade with us. Lisa replied, and expressed his intention to trade, if they did not rate their buffaloe and beaver too high. He then mentioned Mr. Hunt and his party

as his friends, and said he should join them in re-
senting and repelling any injury or insult. Mr. Hunt
declared that the object of his journey was not to
trade, but to see our brothers, at the great salt
lake in the west; and for that undertaking he
should now want horses, as he proposed to go from
thence by land. That he had plenty of goods to
exchange, if they would spare the horses. Mr.
Lisa and Mr. Hunt accompanied their speeches by
suitable presents of tobacco. *Le Gauche* spoke,
and expressed the satisfaction of his people at our
coming, and their attachment to the white men.
In respect to the trade with Mr. Lisa, he wished
for more time, to fix the price of dried buffaloe
skins, (usually called buffaloe robes) the article
they had most of; his present idea of the price was
thirty loads of powder and ball for each robe.
Respecting Mr. Hunt's proposition, he was certain they could not spare the number of horses
that he understood he wanted; and that he did
not think they ought to sell any horses. *Les
Yeux Gris*, another chief, replied to the latter
part of his speech, by stating that they might easily
spare Mr. Hunt a considerable number of horses,
as they could readily replace them by stealing or
by smoking.* These arguments governed the

* It was not difficult to comprehend that horses might be obtained by stealing, but how they could be procured by smoking

opinions of the chiefs, and it was determined to open a trade for horses, when they were satisfied with the price Mr. Hunt purposed to give. The council now broke up, and Messrs. Hunt, M'Kenzie, M'Clellan, Dorion, and myself were conducted to the lodge of one of their chiefs, where there was a feast of sweet corn, prepared by boiling, and mixing it with buffaloe grease. Accustomed as I now was to the privation of bread and salt, I thought it very palatable. *Sweet corn*, is corn gathered before it is ripe, and dried in the sun: it is called by the Americans *green corn*, or *corn in the milk*. I quitted the feast, in order to examine the town, which I found to be fortified all round with a ditch, and with pickets or pallisadoes, of about nine feet high. The lodges are placed without any regard to regularity, which renders it difficult to count them, but there appears to be from 150 to 160, and they are constructed in the same manner as those of the Ottoes, with the additional convenience of a railing on the eaves: be-

---

I did not then understand. On the first opportunity, I enquired from Mr. Crooks, who is remarkably well acquainted with Indian customs; from him I learned, that it is a practice with tribes in amity to apply to each other in cases of necessity. When one tribe is deficient in any article of which the other has abundance, they send a deputation who smoke with them, and inform them of their wants. It would be a breach of Indian courtesy to send them away without the expected supply.

hind this railing they sit at their ease and smoke. There is scarcely any declivity in the scite of the town, and as little regard is paid to cleanliness, it is very dirty in wet weather. I spent the remainder of the day in examining the bluffs, to ascertain what new plants might be collected in the neighbourhood; having now, for the first time in the course of our voyage, an opportunity to preserve living specimens. During this time, the rest of the boats crossed over the river, and a camp was formed about 200 yards below the town. Lisa was nearer to it.

13th.—The morning being rainy, no business could commence in the village until the afternoon, when Mr. Hunt exhibited the kind and quantity of goods he purposed to give for each horse. These were placed in the lodge of *Le Gauche*, for general inspection, and proved to be satisfactory. I this day employed myself in forming a place for the reception of living specimens, a little distance below our camp, and near the river, for the convenience of water.

14th.—I understood that Lisa and the chiefs had agreed that the price of a buffaloe robe should be twenty balls, and twenty loads of powder. He removed a part of his goods to the lodge of *Le Gauche*, and Mr. Hunt began to trade at the lodge of the *Big Man.* The trade for horses soon commenced; the species of goods most in demand were carbines, powder, ball, tomahawks, knives, &c. as another expedition against the Sioux was meditated. Whilst the trading was going on, I walked with Mr. Brackenridge to the upper village, separated from the lower one by a small stream. In our walk through the town, I was accosted by the *Medicine Man,* or doctor, who was standing at the entrance of a lodge, into which we went. It appeared that one of his patients was within, who was a boy, for whom he was preparing some medecine. He made me understand that he had seen me collecting plants, and that he knew me to be a *Medicine Man;* frequently shaking hands, he took down his medicine bag, made of deer skin, and showed me its contents. As I supposed this bag contained the whole *materia medica* of the nation, I examined it with some attention. There was a considerable quantity of the down of reedmace, *(Typha palustris)* which I understood was used in cases of burns or scalds; there was also a quantity of a species of *Artemisia,* common on the prairies, and known to the hunters by the name of *Hyssop,* but that ingredient which was in the greatest abundance, was a species of wall-flower; in character it agrees with *Cheiranthus erysimoides;* besides these, I found two new species of *Astragalus,* and some roots of *Rudbeckia purpurea.* After examining the contents of the bag, I assured the doctor it was all very good, and we again shook hands with him, and went into several other lodges, where we were very hospitably received. Although they sit on the ground round the fire, buffaloe robes were always spread for us, and the pipe was invariably brought out, whilst the squaw prepared something for us to eat; this consisted of dried buffaloe meat, mixed with pounded corn, warmed on the fire in an earthen vessel of their own manufacture: some offered us sweet corn, mixed with beans, (*Phaseolus.*) The squaws were particularly attentive to us, and took every opportunity to examine such parts of our dress as were manufactured, and not of skins. After our return, I went to the trading house, and found that the trade for horses went on very briskly. The instant a horse was bought, his tail was cropped, as they would then be easily distinguished from those belonging to the Indians, which are in all respects as nature formed them. On my return to our camp, I found the warrior there with whom I had become acquainted on the 1st instant. He insisted so much on my going to his lodge, that I went with him; where he spread a very finely painted buffaloe robe for me to sit on, and showed me, by signs, that it was now mine. In return, I gave him a pair of silver bracelets, with ornaments for the ears and hair, having brought a considerable quantity of those articles from St. Louis. With these he was so much pleased, that he requested me to sleep at his lodge during our stay, and informed me that his sister should be my bedfellow. This offer I declined, alledging as an excuse, that I had voluntarily engaged to assist in keeping guard round our camp. I found, on my return, that the principals of our party were engaged in a very serious consultation on our present situation. All our fresh provisions were exhausted, and of the dried buffaloe bought at the Poncars, not more remained than was thought necessary to reserve for the journey by land. A few bags of Indian corn being all that remained, it was thought expedient to apply to the same purpose, to be parched, ground, and mixed with sugar. It had been this day ascertained that the Aricaras could not spare us any provisions, as the excessive rains had penetrated into their *caches,** and spoiled the whole of their reserved stock, so that they expected to be in want themselves before the harvest would come in. In addition to our difficulties, a rumour had been spread this afternoon, and it was believed, that the Sioux had

---

* The nations on the Missouri, always liable to be surprised and plundered by the *Teton* villains, annually conceal a quantity of corn, beans, &c. after harvest, in holes in the ground, which are artfully covered up. These hoards are called by French, *caske,* from the verb *casher,* to hide.

followed us, and were now in the neighbourhood, to the amount of four or five hundred. Whether this was true or not, the consequences were the same to us, as our hunters could not, with any degree of prudence be suffered to go out; nor indeed were they willing. In this dilemma, no means could be thought of for the removal of our difficulties, but to purchase some of the spare dogs from the Indians, particularly those employed in dragging their sledges, and this measure was resolved on. It may be here remarked, that horses and dogs are the only animals which the Indians domesticate: of the latter they have two varieties, one of these they employ in hunting; the other appears to be of a stupid and lazy nature, always remaining about the village, and employed as mentioned above.

15th.—In conformity with the measure determined upon last evening, a number of dogs were purchased this morning, brought to the camp, and shot for breakfast. I went out to collect, accompanied by Mr. Brackenridge, and proceeded farther into the interior than I had before done. I was rewarded by several new species of plants, and by farther confirmation of the geological formations, as the hills situated at a distance from the river have uniformly flat summits, covered with fragments of rock, mixed with smaller stones and gra-

vel. On our return, and when about three miles
from the camp, we saw Indians pouring out from
the village, some on horseback, others on foot, and
all at full speed. They went in a direction to our
right, towards some hills, five or six miles distant
down the river. A young Indian soon after, in
passing us at some distance, changed his course,
and came up to me. He spoke with great earnestness, frequently pointing to the hills, on the
tops of which I observed some horsemen apparently
meeting each other, and after passing turn back,
which was continued gallopping. I at length comprehended that enemies were near, and that seeing
me only armed with a pistol, he wished me to hasten to the camp. When we came nearer the town,
I observed that the tops of the lodges were crowded with women, children, and old men, all looking
earnestly towards the hills, and considerable numbers were still running past our camp. I now enquired the cause of the tumult, and found that a
signal had been given, indicating the appearance of
a war party of the Sioux. The noise and confusion
was such as I have not often witnessed : the war
whoop was heard in every direction, and even the
old men in the village were busily employed in animating the warriors. Some aged Nestors tottered
along with the crowd, raising their shrill voices to
encourage the young and vigorous to exert themselves in repelling the foe. If any enemy really

appeared, they had immediately fled on being discovered, a thing not at all unlikely, as it is conformable to their customs, and in this instance the
more probable, as the Sioux would naturally expect
that our party would join their adversaries. At all
events, the party soon returned in as much disorder
as they went out. I observed, that amongst the warriors of this and the other nations, several had foxes'
tails attached to the heels of their mockasons, and
I am informed by Captain Winter, who resided some
time at Michillimakinac, that the same custom prevails among the tribes in Upper Canada, and that
this honour is only permitted to such warriors as
have killed an enemy on his own ground.

16th.—I went into the village, and found that
the chiefs were assembled to hear from the warriors
an account of what had passed the preceding day.
As they were not *in the habit of printing newspapers*,
the news was carried through the village by heralds,
who stood at the door of the council-lodge, and from
time to time went through the village to give information. On my return to the camp, I found that a ne-
gotiation was going on betwixt Mr. Hunt and Mr.
Lisa respecting the boats belonging to our party,
which were no longer of any use. These Mr. Hunt
was willing to exchange with Mr. Lisa for horses,
of which he had a considerable number at the Fort
belonging to the Missouri Fur Company, about

200 miles higher up the river. Mr. Hunt, some days previous to this, presented to me the smallest boat, which was a barge built at Michillimakinac; and three American hunters, whom we found at the Aricara nation, agreed to assist me in navigating it down the river, when I should be disposed to return. The three other boats, and some Indian goods, were finally exchanged with Mr. Lisa. In consequence of this arrangement, I found that a party were to be dispatched in a few days to the Fort for the horses, and I instantly resolved to accompany them, if permitted. After an excursion to collect plants, I walked into the village in the evening, and found that a party had arrived, who had been on an expedition to steal horses, in which they were successful. This event, and the return of the war party, caused an unusual bustle; the tops of the lodges were crowded with men, women, and children. Several of the old men harangued them in a loud voice. The subject I understood to be an exhortation to behave well towards the white people, and stating the advantages they derived by an intercourse with them. Notwithstanding all this tumult, some of the women continued their employment in dressing the buffaloe skins, which are stretched on frames, and placed on stages, erected both for this purpose and to dry or jerk the flesh of animals cut into thin slices.

17th.—It was determined that Mr. Crooks should
go to the Company's Fort for the horses, and as
more than thirty had been bought from the Aricaras, the men who were to accompany him began to
select from amongst them such as they thought the
best able to perform the journey. Although resolved to accompany them, I did not take the same
precaution. This neglect occasioned me afterwards much vexation. I had already expressed
my wish to undertake the journey, and Mr. Hunt
had not absolutely refused to permit me; but he
tried by arguments to dissuade me from it. He
represented to me the danger which the party ran
of being cut off by the Sioux, the fatigue of riding
on an Indian saddle, &c. I therefore did not for
the present press the subject, excepting to Mr.
Crooks, who knew my determination, and was much
pleased with it. After devoting the greatest part of
the day to the increasing of my collection, I went
into the village, and found that some Indians had
arrived from the Chayenne nation, having been sent
to inform the Aricaras of their intention to visit
them in fifteen days. One of these Indians was
covered with a buffalo robe, curiously ornamented
with figures worked with split quills, stained red
and yellow, intermixed with much taste, and the
border of the robe entirely hung round with the
hoofs of young fawns, which at every movement
made a noise much resembling that of the rattle-

snake when that animal is irritated. I understood that this robe had been purchased from the Arapahoes, or Big Bead Indians, a remote tribe, who frequent the Rocky Mountains. I wished much to purchase the robe, and offered him such articles in exchange as I thought most likely to induce him to part with it, but he refused. The day following it was purchased by Mr. M'Clelland, who gave it to me for silver ornaments and other articles, amounting to about ten dollars. I found that these Indians could not speak the Aricara language, having need of an interpreter. This place was supplied by one of the Aricaras, who could speak their language. They were tall and well proportioned men, but of a darker complexion than the Aricaras. This nation has no fixed place of residence, but resort chiefly about the Black Hills, near the head of Chayenne river, having been driven from their former place of residence, near the Red River of Lake Winnipic, by the Sioux. Their number is now inconsiderable, as they scarcely muster 100 warriors. On my return to the camp, I found it crowded with Indians and squaws, as it had been for the two preceding evenings. Travellers who have been acquainted with savages, have remarked that they are either very liberal of their women to strangers, or extremely jealous. In this species of liberality no nation can be exceeded by the Aricaras, who flocked down every evening with their wives, sisters, and daughters, each anxious to meet with a market for them. The Canadians were very good customers, and Mr. Hunt was kept in full employ during the evening, in delivering out to them blue beads and vermillion, the articles in use for this kind of traffic. This evening I judged that there were not fewer than eighty squaws, and I observed several instances wherein the squaw was consulted by her husband as to the *quantum sufficit* of price, a mark of consideration which, from some knowledge of Indians, and the estimation in which their women are held, I had not expected.

18th.—Went early to the bluffs to the south-westward of the town, on one of which I observed fourteen buffaloe skulls placed in a row. The cavities of the eyes and the nostrils were filled with a species of *artemisia* common on the prairies, which appears to be a non-descript. On my return I caused our interpreter to enquire into the reason for this, and found that it was an honour conferred on the buffaloes which they had killed, in order to appease their spirits, and prevent them from apprising the living buffaloes of the danger they run in approaching the neighbourhood. After my return I walked into the village with Mr. Donald M'Kenzie, who wore a green surtout. This attracted very much the attention of the squaws, and from the surprise they shewed, I believe it is a colour they were unacquainted with. They were so anxious to obtain a part of it, that several offered him *favours* as an equivalent for a piece which they marked out. This occasioned much mirth betwixt us, and on my part a pretended alarm for fear that his coat should become a *spencer.* We amused ourselves some time by watching a party who were engaged in play. A place was neatly formed, resembling a skittle alley, about nine feet in breadth and ninety feet long: a ring of wood, about five inches in diameter, was trundled along from one end, and when it had run some distance, two Indians, who stood ready, threw after it, in a sliding manner, each a piece of wood, about three feet long and four inches in breadth, made smooth on one edge, and kept from turning by a cross piece passing through it, and bended backwards so as to resemble a cross bow. The standers by kept an account of the game, and he whose piece, in a given number of throws, more frequently came nearest the ring after it had fallen, won the game.

19th.—We breakfasted early, having killed the dogs the night before, and ten horses were brought into the camp for the party appointed to go to the fort, beyond the Mandans, to escort the horses agreed for with Mr. Lisa, and I now declared to Mr. Hunt that, unless he absolutely refused me

the privilege, I was determined to accompany them.
With his accustomed kindness he consented, and a
man was dispatched to catch a horse for me on the
Prairie. As the party had cast their bullets, and
made every other preparation the preceding night,
we were all ready, when the man returned with
a very bad horse. He was small, and apparently
weak; but being unwilling to delay the party, I
fixed my saddle, and we set out, having previously
agreed with one of the men to take care of my
plants in my absence. We had for our guide a
person of the name of Jones, who was acquainted
with the whole of the country betwixt the Mandans and Aricaras; and after passing the villages,
kept as much as possible in the ravines and valleys,
to avoid being seen by the Sioux Indians, who
we had reason to think were still lurking about the
country; as we knew that if they discovered us, they
would, almost to a certainty, cut us off. As there
were no provisions to spare in the camp, except a
little dog's flesh, we took nothing with us to eat,
nor made the least attempt to look for game, as
our safety perhaps depended on the celerity and
silence of our march; we continued at a smart
trot until near eight o'clock in the evening, having
only stopped once to give the horses an opportunity to feed. Our course lay nearly north, and
we kept the river in sight the whole of the day,
sometimes very near it, and at other times five or

six miles distant. We encamped on the border of
a creek, not more than a mile from the Missouri,
on the open prairie. We found this place so much
infested with mosquitoes that scarcely any of us slept.
In the latter part of the day, I began to discover the
insufficiency of my horse, as it was with difficulty
I could keep up with the rest. The reflections on
my situation, combined with the pain occasioned by
mosquitoes, kept me from closing my eyes; in addition to this, I had already painfully experienced
the effects of an Indian saddle, which I shall describe. It consists of six pieces of wood ; two of
these are strong forked sticks, one of which is
formed to fix on the shoulders of the horse, the
other is adapted to the lower part of the back ;
they are connected by four flat pieces, each about
four inches in breadth ; two of these are so placed
as to lie on each side of the backbone of the horse,
which rises above them ; the two others are fastened to the extremities of the forked sticks, and
the whole is firmly tied by thongs. Two strong
slips of buffaloe hide are doubled over each of the
upper connecting pieces, for the purpose of holding the stirrup, which is formed of a stick about
two feet long, and cut half way through in two
places, so as to divide it into three equal parts ; at
these places it is bent, and when the two ends are
strongly tied, it forms an equilateral-triangle. The
conjunct end of the foremost forked stick rises to

the height of eight or ten inches above the back of
the horse, and serves to fasten on it the coiled end
of the long slip of dried skin intended to serve as
a bridle : this slip is also made use of to fasten the
horse at night, to allow him sufficient space wherein to graze, and is mostly fifty or sixty feet long.
Under the saddle is laid a square piece of buffaloe
skin, dressed with the hair upon it, and doubled
four-fold, and on the saddle the rider fixes his
blanket.

20th.—We were on horseback on the first appearance of day, and immediately abandoned the
river, passed over the bluffs, and struck into the
interior of the country. Besides my rifle and other
equipments, similar to those of the rest of the party,
I had a portfolio for securing the specimens of plants.
I had contrived already to collect some interesting
specimens by frequently alighting to pluck them,
and put them into my hat. For these opportunities,
and to ease my horse, I ran many miles alongside of
him. Notwithstanding this, about noon he seemed
inclined to give up, and I proposed to Mr. Crooks
that I should turn back : this he would by no means
agree to, but prevailed on the lightest man in company to exchange horses with me for the rest of
the day. Soon after noon, some deer were observed
grazing at a distance, and we halted in a small valley, suffered the horses to graze, and one of the

men was dispatched to look after them, who soon returned, having killed one. As we had not eaten any thing from the morning of the preceding day, this news was very acceptable, and some were dispatched to fetch the meat, whilst others gathered dry buffaloe dung to boil our kettle. This opportunity afforded me the pleasure of adding to my little collection, besides securing in my portfolio what I had before gathered. It is perhaps needless to observe that the men were not slow in bringing the meat, nor that we were equally expeditious in our cooking. We were so confident of finding game that we did not take any part of what remained, but proceeded in the hope of being able to reach Cannon-ball river,* intending to encamp on its banks. In the course of the afternoon, we began to perceive innumerable herds of buffaloe ; and had we wished to hunt, we might have killed great numbers ; but we avoided them as much as possible, for fear of disturbing them, as it might have been the means of enabling some lurking war party to discover us. It is well known to the hunters and the Indians, that a herd of buffaloe, when

---

* Cannon-ball river derives its name from the singularly round form of the stones which are found in its bed. These are of all sizes, from one to twelve inches in diameter, or sometimes more; they are of a brownish sand-stone, and before they were rounded by attrition, must have been formed in cubes.

frightened, will often run 10, 15, or even 20 miles before they stop. About five o'clock we perceived before us the valley of Cannon-ball river, bounded on each side by a range of small hills, visible as far as the eye can reach, and as they appear to diminish regularly, in the proportion of their distance, they produce a singular and pleasing effect. As the evening approached, and as we considered the danger from the Sioux much decreased, we ventured to kill a buffaloe: each man cut what he thought proper, and the remainder was left for the wolves, who doubtless picked the bones before the morning. On descending into the valley of the river, some deer were observed, feeding near the bank, whilst others were lying down near them. Some of our men stole cautiously round a grove of timber, and shot two of the poor animals, although we had no great occasion for them. The Cannon-ball river was muddy at this time; but whether it is constantly so or not, I could not learn. It is here about 160 yards wide, but so shallow that we crossed it without swimming, but not without wetting some of the blankets, on our saddles. We encamped on a very fine prairie, near the river, affording grass in abundance, nearly a yard high, in which we stationed our horses. The alluvion of the river is about a mile in breadth from bluff to bluff, and is very beautiful, being prairie, interspersed with groves of trees, and ornamented with beautiful plants, now in flower. Amongst others which I did not observe before, I found a species of flax, resembling that which is cultivated: I think it is the species known as *Linum Perenne.* I rambled until it was quite dark, and found my way to the camp by observing the fire.

21st.—We arose before day. Each man cooked his own breakfast, cutting what suited him from the venison, and fixing it on a stick set in the ground, which inclined over the fire. At break of day we were on horseback, and soon after ascended the bluffs, and proceeded on our route. I noticed a sensible change in the face of the country, after we had left the river. We now found some of the more elevated places covered with small stones, and divested of herbage, and throughout, the soil was of less depth, and the grass shorter and more scanty. About ten o'clock we again found the country to assume the same fertile appearance as on the preceding day; and saw herds of buffaloe in every direction : before mid-day two were killed, but very little was taken, except the marrow-bones; each man, who chose to take one, hung it to his saddle. In the course of this forenoon we observed three rattle-snakes, of an entirely new and undescribed species; one of them I killed and carried in my shot-pouch, and during the time we stopped to feed our horses, I secured the skin. We passed

very close to several herds of buffaloe during the
afternoon, near which we always observed a number of wolves lurking. I perceived that those
herds that had wolves in their vicinity, were almost
wholly females with their calves ; but noticed also,
that there were a few bulls with them, and that
these were always stationed at the outside of the
herd, inclosing the cows with their calves within.
We came suddenly on one of these herds, containing, as we judged, from six to eight hundred ; they
immediately gallopped off; one of our party rode
after them, and overtook a calf which could not
keep pace with the rest : he instantly dismounted,
caught it by the hind leg, and plunged his knife
into its body. We took what we wanted, and rode
on. This afternoon I noticed a singularly-form-
ed hill on our right, in the direction of the Missouri, apparently about 10 miles from us. It is of
an oblong shape, nearly perpendicular at the ends,
and level at the top, so as to resemble a regular
building : near the centre there rises a pic, very
steep, which seems to be elevated at least 100 feet
above the hill on which it stands. We rode this
day almost without intermission, and late in the
evening arrived at *Rivière de Cœur*, or Heart
River, and encamped on its banks, or, more properly, lay down in our blankets. I found that my
horse did not get worse, although he showed a great
disposition to lag behind, a certain proof of his

being very much tired, as the Indian horses, when on a journey, have an aversion to be separated from their companions.

22nd.—Although the distance from this place to the Missouri Fur Company's fort was estimated at about sixty miles, we determined, if possible to reach it this day, and were, as usual, on horseback at day-break, having previously breakfasted on veal. I observed the preceding days a sufficient number of buffaloes to induce me to credit the hunters in their reports of the vast numbers they had seen, but this day afforded me ample confirmation. Scarcely had we ascended the bluffs of Heart River, when we began to discern herds in every direction ; and had we been disposed to devote the day to hunting, we might have killed a great number, as the country north of Heart River is not so uniform in its surface as that we had passed. It consists of ridges, of small elevation, separated by narrow vallies. This renders it much more favourable for hunting, and although we did not materially deviate from our course, five were killed before noon. Mr. Crooks joined me in remonstrating against this waste ; but it is impossible to restrain the hunters, as they scarcely ever lose an opportunity, if it offers, even although not in want of food. About two o'clock we arrived on the summit of a ridge more elevated than any we had yet passed. From thence we saw before us a beautiful plain, as we judged, about four miles across, in the direction of our course, and of similar dimension from east to west. It was bounded on all sides by long ridges, similar to that which we had ascended. The scene exhibited in this valley was sufficiently interesting to excite even in our Canadians a wish to stop a few minutes and contemplate it. The whole of the plain was perfectly level, and, like the rest of the country, without a single shrub. It was covered with the finest verdure, and in every part herds of buffaloe were feeding. I counted seventeen herds, but the aggregate number of the animals it was difficult even to guess at : some thought upwards of 10,000. We descended into the plain, and each having two marrow bones hung to his saddle, we resolved to dine wherever we could first find water. In descending into the plain we came upon a small herd feeding in a valley. One was shot by our party before we could possibly restrain them. At about half the distance across the plain we reached a small pond, where we halted, and having collected a sufficient quantity of dry buffaloe's dung, we made a fire, in which we disposed our bones, and although the water was stagnant, we made free use of it. During our stay here a very large herd of buffaloes continued to feed within a quarter of a mile of us. Some of them I observed to gaze at

us, but as they were to the windward, they had
not the power of discovering what we were by the
sense of smelling. I found, on enquiry from some
of our party who were well acquainted with the
habits of that animal, that it seems to rely chiefly
on that sense for its safety. Around this herd we
counted fifteen wolves, several of which stood for
some minutes looking at us, without exhibiting
any signs of fear; and as we did not think them
worth shooting, we left them unmolested. On
gaining the summit of the ridge forming the northern boundary of the plain, we noticed a chain of
hills on our right hand, at the distance of about six
miles. Jones, our guide, assured us they were the
bluffs of the Missouri, and although we might not
be able to reach the Fort that night, yet he was certain of our being able to go to the Mandan village.
About four o'clock we fell into a trace that Jones
said was one of the roads which the Mandans usually followed when they went out to hunt. We
determined to keep along it, as we found it led us
towards the bluffs, at which we arrived in about
an hour, and passed through a narrow valley,
bounded on each side by some small rocks of secondary limestone. On turning an angle in the
valley, we came suddenly in view of the Missouri,
at no great distance from us. The sight of the
river caused much joy in our party; but no one had
so much occasion as myself to be pleased with it,

as it was with the greatest difficulty I could keep up with the party, my horse being so tired, that Dorion, our interpreter, and others of the party occasionally rode after me, to beat him forward. The trace turned up a long and very fine plain, betwixt the bluffs and the river. The plain continued to increase in breadth as we advanced, and had on it a sufficiency of clumps of cotton wood so interspersed as to prevent our seeing its upper termination. We had not been on this plain more than half an hour, when we suddenly saw an Indian on horseback, gallopping down the bluffs at full speed, and in a few minutes he was out of sight, having proceeded nearly in the same direction we were pursuing. We considered this as a certain proof that we were not far from the Mandan town, and not long after, on turning round the point of a large grove, we came in full view of it. We could perceive that the Indian had already given notice of our approach, as the tops of the lodges were crowded with people ; and shortly after, as we advanced, we saw crowds coming from the town to meet us. From the time the first of the Indians met us till we arrived in the town, we were continually employed in shaking hands, as every one was eager to perform that ceremony with the whole party, and several made us understand that they had seen us before, having been of the war party which we had met at the Great Bend. They con-

K

ducted us to the lodge of She-he-ké, the chief,
where we alighted. He met us at the door, and
after shaking hands with us, to my great surprise
he said in English, " come in house." I was again
surprised at one of the first objects that met my
view on entering the lodge, it was a fine dunghill
cock. On enquiry I found that She-he-ké. had
brought it with him from the United States at the
time he accompanied Messrs. Lewis and Clark,
where also he learnt his English. It appeared that
immediately on the centinel announcing our approach, the squaw had *set on the pot.* As the vic-
tuals were ready before we had done smoking, and
as Mr. Crooks expressed a determination that we
should proceed to the Missouri Fur Company's
Fort this evening, we soon finished our meal, consisting of jerked flesh of buffaloe and pounded
corn. The sun was setting when we mounted, and
several of our horses began to appear much jaded,
but mine in particular. I therefore proposed to remain at the Mandans ; but the party, and in
particular Mr. Crooks, wished me to go on. With
some reluctance I consented, and we pushed on
our horses, in order to reach Knife River before
it was quite dark, which by much exertion we effected, and arrived opposite to the third village of
the *Minetaree,* or *Gros Ventres Indians,* as the
night was closing in. On hallooing, some Indians
came down to the bank of the river opposite to us,

and immediately ran back to the village. In a few minutes we saw them returning along with six squaws, each of whom had a skin canoe on her back, and a paddle in her hand. Whilst we unsaddled our horses they crossed the river, and the Indians swam over, and all shook hands with us. The squaws placed our saddles in the canoes, where we also disposed ourselves, leaving the Indians to drive our horses over the river, which they managed with much address, by placing themselves in such a way as to keep them in a compact body. This river is not rapid, but has the appearance of being deep, and is about eighty yards wide at this place. After saddling our horses, and giving the squaws three balls and three loads of powder for each man, being the price of ferriage, we passed through the village, having seven miles still to travel in order to reach the Fort :—we could not now make our horses exceed a walk. I observed on the hill above the town the appearance of cavalry, which could be only imperfectly distinguished. These Jones told me were the stages whereon they deposit the bodies of their dead. About eleven o'clock we reached the Fort, after having travelled this day more than eighteen hours, with very little intermission. We were received in a very friendly manner by Mr. Reuben Lewis, brother to Captain Lewis, who travelled to the Pacific Ocean. The mosquitoes were much less friendly to us, and were in such numbers, and so troublesome, that notwithstanding our excessive fatigue, it was next to impossible to sleep.

23rd.—We went early to look at the horses. The greater part were lying down, and it appeared had scarcely moved from the place where they had been left the preceding night, seeming to prefer rest to food. In consequence of their jaded state, Mr. Crooks resolved to remain at the Fort four or five days, that they might recruit themselves. On our return to breakfast, we found that the Fort was but ill supplied with provisions, having little of any thing but jerked meat; but as that, or any other accommodation the place afforded, was accompanied by kindness and the most polite attention from Mr. Lewis, we were much pleased with our reception. The bluffs here have a very romantic appearance, and I was preparing to examine them after breakfast, when some squaws came in belonging to the uppermost village of the Minetarees, with a quantity of roots to sell. Being informed that they were dug on the prairie, my curiosity was excited, and on tasting I found them very palatable, even in a raw state. They were of the shape of an egg, some nearly as large as that of a goose, others smaller. Mr. Lewis obligingly caused some to be boiled. The taste most resembled that of a parsnip, but I thought them much better. I found no vestige of the plant attached to them, and anxious to ascertain the species, I succeeded in obtaining information from the squaws of the route by which they came to the Fort, and immediately set out on the search. After much pains I found one of the places where they had dug the plants, and to my surprise discovered, from the tops broken off, that the plant was one I was well acquainted with, having found it even in the vicinity of St. Louis, where I had first discovered it, and determined it to be a new species of *Psoralea,* which is now known as *Psoralea esculenta.* On enquiry I was informed that this root is of the greatest importance, not only to the Indians, but to the hunters, who, in case of the failure of other food, from the want of success in hunting, can always support life by resorting to it ; and even when not impelled by want, it cannot but be extremely grateful to those who otherwise must exist on animal food alone, without bread or salt; at least I then thought it so. I found the country about the Fort, and especially the bluffs, extremely interesting. It chiefly consists of argillaceous schistus, and a very tenacious and indurated yellow clay, exhibiting in many places the appearance of coal. The land floods from the country behind the bluffs had cut through them, and left large bodies of clay standing up, with the sides perpendicular, and resembling in appearance towers, or large square buildings, which it was impossible to ascend. The incumbent soil appears to be of excellent quality, and was at this time covered with fine grass and a number of beautiful plants. The roots and specimens of these I collected with the greatest assiduity, not having yet determined to remain any longer than until our party returned. I soon found the number to increase so much as I lengthened my excursions, that I resolved to remain at the Fort until Mr. Lisa came up with his boat, and obtain a passage with him down to the Aricaras, and this resolution I announced to Mr. Crooks. The Missouri had overflowed its banks some time before our arrival, and on receding it had left numberless pools in the alluvion. In these the mosquitoes had been generated in numbers inconceivably great. In walking it was necessary to have one hand constantly employed to keep them out of the eyes; and although a person killed hundreds, thousands were ready to take their place. At evening the horses collected in a body round the Fort, waiting until fires were made, to produce smoke, in which they might stand for protection. This was regularly done, and a quantity of green weeds thrown on each fire to increase the smoke. These fires caused much quarrelling and fighting, each horse contending for the centre of the smoke and the place nearest the fire. In the afternoon we were visited by She-he-kè, the Mandan chief, who came dressed in a suit of clothes brought with him from the United States. He informed us that he had a great wish to go live with the whites, and that several of his people, induced by the representations he had made of the white people's mode of living, had the same intentions. We were able to converse with She-he-kè through the medium of Jussum, the interpreter for the Fort, who was a Frenchman, and had married a squaw belonging to the second village of the Minetarees, or Gros Ventres Indians. As I expressed a wish to visit the villages, I spoke to Jussum on that subject, who readily consented to accompany me, but informed me that in a day or two there would be a dance of the squaws, to celebrate the exploits of their husbands, when it was agreed we should go. The Fort consisted of a square block-house, the lower part of which was a room for furs: the upper part was inhabited by Mr. Lewis and some of the hunters belonging to the establishment. There were some small outhouses, and the whole was surrounded by a pallisado, or piquet, about fifteen feet high. I found attached to it a very pretty garden, in which were peas, beans, sallad, radishes, and other vegetables, under the care of a gardener, an Irishman, who shewed it to me with much self-importance. I praised his management, but expressed my regret that he had no potatoes. " Oh!" said he, " that does not signify ; we can soon have them ; there is plenty just over the way." I did not think the

man was serious; but on mentioning the circumstance to Mr. Lewis, he told me that there really
were potatoes at an English Fort on the river St.
Peters, *only* from two to 300 miles distant.

24th.—This morning I was informed by Jussum
that the squaw dance would be performed in the afternoon, and he promised to have horses ready for
us by mid-day. I packed up a few beads for presents, and spent the fore part of the day in my
usual way, but took a more extended range into
the interior from the river, as the air was calm,
having already discovered that the mosquitoes remained almost entirely in the valley of the river,
where during calm weather it was almost impossible
to collect. On the top of a hill, about four miles
from the Fort, I had a fine view of a beautiful valley, caused by a rivulet, being a branch of Knife
River, the declivities of which abound in a new
species of *Eleagnus*, intermixed with a singular
procumbent species of cedar *(Juniperus.)* The
branches are entirely prostrate on the ground, and
never rise above the height of a few inches. The
beautiful silvery hue of the first, contrasted with
the dark green of the latter, had a most pleasing
effect; and to render the scene more interesting,
the small alluvion of the rivulet was so plentifully
covered with a species of lilly *(Lilium catesbæi)*, as
to make it resemble a scarlet stripe as far as the

eye cou'd trace it. I returned to the Fort much gratified, and prepared to accompany Jussum to the dance. On our approach some fields of Indian corn lay betwixt us and the village, which I wished to avoid, and proposed that we should change our route, as the corn was now nearly a yard high.* This proposal was absolutely refused by Jussum, and we rode on through the corn till we came to where some squaws were at work, who called out to us to make us change our route, but were soon silenced by Jussum. I suspected that he committed this aggression to show his authority or importance. On our arrival at the village we went into several of the lodges, and I found them con-

* This is about the full height to which the maize grows in the Upper Missouri, and when this circumstance is connected with the quickness with which it grows and is matured, it is a wonderful instance of the power given to some plants to accommodate themselves to climate. The latitude of this place is about 47 degrees geographically, but geologically many degrees colder, arising from its elevation, which must be admitted to be very considerable, when we consider that it is at a distance of more than 3000 miles from the ocean by the course of a rapid river. This plant is certainly the same species of *Zea* that is cultivated within the tropics, where it usually requires four months to ripen, and rises to the height of twelve feet. Here ten weeks is sufficient, with a much less degree of heat. Whether or not this property is more peculiar to plants useful to men, and given for wise and benevolent purposes, I will not attempt to determine.

structed exactly in the same form as those of the
Aricaras. We smoked at every lodge, and I found
by the bustle among the women that they were
preparing for the dance, as some of them were
putting on their husbands clothes, for which purpose they did not retire into a corner, nor seem
in the least discomposed by our presence. In
about half an hour the dance began, which was
performed in a circle, the dancers moving round,
with tomahawks in their hands. At intervals
they turned their faces all at once towards the
middle of the circle, and brandished their weapons.
After some time one of them stepped into the
centre of the ring, and made an harangue, frequently brandishing her weapon, whilst the rest
moved round her. I found that the nature of all
the speeches was the same, which was to boast of
the actions of their husbands. One which caused
Jussum to smile I requested he would interpret.
He briefly informed me, that she had said her husband had travelled south-west to a country inhabited by white people, which journey took him
twenty days to perform: that he went to steal horses, and when he came to the white people's houses,
he found one where the men were gone out, and
in which he killed two women, and stole from them
a number of horses. She corrected herself, by
denying that they were women whom her husband
had killed, and the reasons she assigned to prove

they were not, was what caused Jussum to smile. The dance did not last more than an hour, and I was informed by Jussum that it would be followed by a feast of dog's flesh, of which it was expected I should partake. I excused myself by saying I wished to collect some plants, and set out alone. In my way to the Fort I passed through a small wood, where I discovered a stage constructed betwixt four trees, standing very near each other, and to which the stage was attached, about ten feet from the ground. On this stage was laid the body of an Indian, wrapt in a buffalo robe. As the stage was very narrow, I could see all that was upon it without much trouble. It was the body of a man, and beside it there lay a bow and quiver with arrows, a tomahawk, and a scalping knife. There were a great number of stages erected about a quarter of a mile from the village, on which the dead bodies were deposited, which, for fear of giving offence, I avoided, as I found, that although it is the custom of these people thus to expose the dead bodies of their ancestors, yet they have in a very high degree that veneration for their remains which is a characteristic of the American Indians. I arrived at the Fort about sunset. Soon afterwards we heard the report of a swivel down the river, which caused us all to run out, and soon saw the boat belonging to Mr. Lisa turning a point about two miles below us. We returned the salute, but he did not arrive that night, as the side on which we were, to within half a mile of the Fort, consisted of high perpendicular bluffs, and his men were too much exhausted to reach us by the river.

25th.—This morning I had the pleasure of again meeting Mr. Brackenridge, and of finding that it was the intention of Mr. Lisa to stay at least a fortnight at the Fort. I was very glad to have so good an opportunity of examining this interesting country. I received by the hands of Mr. Brackenridge some small articles for trade, which I had delivered to him at the Aricaras. This enabled me to reward the gardener for his civility in offering me a place in the garden where I could deposit my living plants, and of this I availed myself during my stay.

27th.—The business relative to the horses having been arranged betwixt Mr. Lisa and Mr. Crooks, he set out early this morning on his return to the Aricara nation; and as he was not without his fears that the Gros Ventres Indians, headed by Le Borgne, or One Eyed, would attempt to rob him of his horses, he determined to proceed with as much celerity as we had travelled to the Fort, and kept his departure as secret as possible. I was much pleased to see this chief at the Fort in a few hours afterwards, being satisfied that Mr. Crooks was now out of his reach. As it may give some idea of the tyrannic sway with which the chiefs sometimes govern these children of nature, I shall relate an instance of cruelty and oppression practised by this villain. He had a wish to possess the wife of a young warrior of his tribe, who was esteemed beautiful. She resisted his offers, and avoided him. He took the opportunity of the absence of her husband, and carried her off forcibly. The husband was informed on his return of the transaction, and went to the lodge of Le Borgne to claim his wife. The monster killed him. The young man had no father : his mother only was living, and he was her only son. The shock deprived her of reason, and she reviles the wretch whenever she meets him, and often seeks him to procure the opportunity of doing so. Even amongst those we term savages, the horror which the deed has occasioned is so great, and the pity which the situation of the poor maniac has excited so prevailing, that he dares not kill her. How much then ought Christians to detest a similar deed. He has a most savage and ferocious aspect, and is of large stature. He is chief of one of the villages of the Minetarees, or, as the French call them, Gros Ventres, and assumes a dominion over both, although there are several other chiefs. It is stated by Mr. Lewis that the two villages or bands can raise 600 warriors, but the number at this time is probably much less. The object of this wretch in visiting the Fort was to make professions of friendship, and to obtain a present. Mr. Lisa knew very well the value of his professions, but, notwithstanding, he gave him some, with which he appeared satisfied.

28th.—Having selected some silver ornaments which I purposed to present to She-he-kè, Mr. Brackenridge agreed to accompany me to the Mandan village. We obtained horses from Mr. Lewis for the journey, and about ten o'clock set off. We crossed Knife River at the lower of the Minetaree villages, and paid the accustomed price to the squaw who ferried us over; for each of us three balls and three charges of powder. Before we left the village, we were invited into the lodge belonging to the *White Wolf,* one of the chiefs of this village, with whom we smoked. I was surprised to observe that his squaw and one of his children had brown hair, although their skins did not appear to be lighter coloured than the rest of the tribe. As the woman appeared to be above forty years of age, it is almost certain that no intercourse had taken place betwixt these people and the whites at the time she was born. I should have been less surprised at the circumstance had they been one of those tribes who change their places of residence; but they have not even a tradition of having resided in any other place than where the present village stands. The *White Wolf* appeared to be much pleased with our visit, and by signs invited us to call at his lodge whenever we came that way. He shook hands very cordially with us at parting. In our way to the Mandans we passed through the small village belonging to the Ahwahhaways, consisting of not more than eighteen or twenty lodges. This nation can scarcely muster fifty warriors, and yet they carry on an offensive war against the Snake and Flathead Indians. On our arrival at the Mandans, She-he-kè, as before, came to the door of his lodge, and said, " come in house." We had scarcely entered when he looked earnestly at us, and said, " whiskey." In this we could not gratify him, as we had not thought of bringing any. I presented the silver ornaments to him, with which he seemed much pleased, and after smoking we were feasted with a dish consisting of jerked buffalo meat, corn, and beans boiled together. I mentioned to him my wish to purchase some mockasons, and he sent out into the village to inform the squaws, who flocked into the lodge in such numbers, and with so plentiful a supply, that I could not buy a tenth part. I furnished myself with a dozen pair at a cheap rate, for which I gave a little vermillion, or rather red lead, and a few strings of blue beads. During our stay, She-he-kè, pointing to a little boy in the lodge whom we had not before noticed, gave us to understand that his father was one of the party that accompanied Mr. Lewis, and also indicated the individual. On our return we crossed Knife River at the upper village of the Minetarees. The old squaw who brought the canoe to the opposite side of the river, to fetch us over, was accompanied by three young squaws, apparently about fourteen or fifteen years of age, who came over in the canoe, and were followed by an Indian, who swam over to take care of our horses. When our saddles were taken off, and put into the canoe, Mr. Brackenridge and myself stepped in, and were followed by the old squaw, when the three young squaws instantly stripped, threw their clothes into the canoe, and jumped into the river. We had scarcely embarked before they began to practice on us every mischievous trick they could think of. The slow progress which the canoe made enabled them to swim round us frequently, sometimes splashing us; then seizing hold of the old squaw's paddle, who tried in vain to strike them with it; at other times they would pull the canoe in such a manner as to change the direction of its course; at length they all seized hold of the hind part, and hung to it. The old squaw called out to the Indian who was following our horses: he immediately swam down to our assistance, and soon relieved us from our frolicksome tormentors, by plunging them successively over head, and holding them for a considerable

time under water. After some time they all made
their escape from him, by diving and swimming in
different directions. On landing, by way of retaliation, we seized their clothes, which caused much
laughing betwixt the squaw and the Indian. We
had many invitations to have staid to smoke, but
as it was near sunset, and we had seven miles to
ride, they excused us.

29th and 30th.—Continued to add to my stock,
and the latter day observed a vein of fine coal,
about eighteen inches thick, in the perpendicular
bluff below the Fort. On shewing some specimens
of it to some of the hunters in the Fort, they assured me it was a very common substance higher
up the river, and that there were places in which
it was on fire. As pumice is often found floating
down the Missouri, I had made frequent enquiries
of the hunters if any volcano existed on the river or
its branches, but could not procure from them any
information that would warrant such a conclusion.
It is probable, therefore, that this pumice stone
proceeds from these burning coal beds.

1st July.—I extended my researches up the
river, along the foot of the bluffs; and when at
the distance of three or four miles from the Fort,
and in the act of digging up some roots, I was
surprised by an Indian, who was within a few yards

of me before I perceived him. He had a short gun on his shoulder, and came close to me. He shewed me by signs that he knew very well I was collecting those roots and plants for medicine, and immediately laying hold of my shirt, he made the motion usual when traffic or exchange is proposed. It consists in crossing the two fore fingers one over the-other alternately. On his pointing to a little distance from us, I perceived a squaw coming up, followed by two dogs, each of which drew a sledge, containing some mockasons and other small articles. The signs which he afterwards made were of a nature not to be misunderstood, and implied a wish to make a certain exchange for my shirt, wherein the squaw would have been the temporary object of barter. To this proposition I did not accede, but replied, in the Osage language, *Honkoska,* (no) which he seemed to understand, and immediately took hold of my belt, which was of scarlet worsted, worked with blue and white beads, and made the same proposition, but with the same success. After looking at me fiercely for a few moments, he took his gun from his shoulder, and said in French, *Sacre Crapaud,* which was also repeated by the squaw. I had foreseen that he would be offended at my refusal, and on the first movement which he made with his gun, I took care to be beforehand with him, by placing my hand on the lock of mine, which I held presented to him. In this situation we gradually withdrew from each other, and he disappeared with his squaw and the dogs.

2nd.—Mr. Brackenridge and myself made an excursion into the interior from the river, and found nothing interesting but what has already been noticed, excepting some bodies of argillaceous schist, some parts of which had a columnar appearance. They were lying in an horizontal position, having something the appearance of the bodies of trees.

4th.—This day being the anniversary of the independence of the United States, Mr. Lisa invited us to dine on board of his boat, and Messrs. Brackenridge, Lewis, Nuttall, and myself attended him, and as Le Borgne and the Black Shoe, the two Minetaree chiefs, called at the Fort before dinner, they were invited also. They ate with moderation, and behaved with much propriety, seeming studiously to imitate the manners of white people. After dinner Mr. Lisa gave to each of the chiefs a glass of whiskey, which they drank without any hesitation; but on having swallowed it, they laid their hands on their stomachs, and exhibited such distortion of features as to render it impossible to forbear laughing. As Jussum was present, I asked him the meaning of some words which they spoke

to each other, when he informed me that they called the whiskey fire water.

As Mr. Lisa announced to us his intention to
depart on the 6th for the Aricaras, I employed
myself during the 5th in packing up carefully my
collection, and on the morning of the 6th we set
out. Our progress down the river was very rapid,
as it was still in a high state. We did not land
until evening, after making in the course of the
day more than 100 miles. In the evening and
during the night the mosquitoes were exceedingly
troublesome, and rendered it almost impossible to
sleep.

7th.—We passed Cannon-ball river about ten
o'clock, and stopped a short time at its mouth,
where I noticed and procured some additional specimens. In the evening I had again the pleasure
of meeting my former companions, and was re-
joiced to find that Mr. Crooks had arrived safe with
the horses, and that Mr. Hunt had now obtained
nearly eighty in all. Soon after my arrival, Mr.
Hunt informed me of his intention to depart from
the Aricaras shortly. I therefore purposed to return down the river; and as the Canadians could
not be permitted to take their trunks, or, as they
termed them, their *caisettes*, by land, I purchased
from them seventeen, in which I purposed to ar-

range my living specimens, having now collected several thousands. It had been a custom with us to keep a guard round our camp during the night since our arrival at the Aricaras. Four of the party were stationed for this purpose until midnight, and were then relieved by four others, who remained on guard until morning. On the morning of the 10th, at day-break, some Indians came to our camp from the village, amongst whom was my friend the young warrior. As I happened to be on guard, he came to me, and by signs invited me to go and breakfast with him. Whilst we were sitting together, he suddenly jumped up, and pointed to the bluffs, at the distance of three or four miles down the river. On looking, I observed a numerous crowd of Indians. He gave me to understand that it was a war party on their return, and immediately ran to the village. In a few minutes the tops of the lodges were crowded with Indians, who appeared much agitated. Soon after an Indian gallopped past our camp, who I understood was a chief. In a few minutes afterwards parties began to come out of the village, on their way to meet the warriors, or rather to join them, as it is the custom for a war party to wait at a distance from the village when a victory has been gained, that their friends may join in the parade of a triumphal entry; and on such occasions all their finery and decorations are displayed: some time also is requisite to enable the warriors at home and their friends to paint themselves, so as to appear with proper eclat. During the time that elapsed before the arrival of the procession, I walked into the village, where an universal stillness prevailed. No business seemed to be going on, excepting the preparing of something for the warriors to eat on their return. The squaws were employed in that business in all the lodges into which I entered,* and I noticed that not one of the poor squaws seemed in the least solicitous about her own person: they are too insignificant to be thought an appen-

---

* I noticed over their fires much larger vessels of earthenware than any I had before seen, and was permitted to examine them. They were sufficiently hardened by the fire to cause them to emit a sonorous tone on being struck, and in all I observed impressions on the outside seemingly made by wicker work. This led me to enquire of them by signs how they were made? when a squaw brought a basket, and taking some clay, she began to spread it very evenly within it, shewing me at the same time that they were made in that way. From the shape of these vessels, they must be under the necessity of burning the basket to disengage them, as they are wider at the bottom than at the top. I must here remark, that at the Great Salt Lick, or Saline, about twenty miles from the mouth of the Wabash, vast quantities of Indian earthenware are found, on which I have observed impressions exactly similar to those here mentioned. From the situation of these heaps of fragments, and their proximity to the salt works, I am decidedly of opinion that the Indians practised the art of evaporating the brine, to make salt, before the discovery of America.

dage to a triumph. It was nearly the middle of the day before the procession came in sight, when I went to meet it, in order that my view might be prolonged. A number of the old men and squaws were also moving down from the town, to meet them. At the head of the procession were four standard bearers, followed by a band of warriors on foot; after which came a party on horseback : to these succeeded two of the principal chiefs, betwixt whom was a young warrior, who I understood had been severely wounded. Then came two other standard bearers, who were succeeded by another band of foot and horse, which order was observed until the four bands of which the party consisted had passed. They were about 300 in number : each man carried a shield ; a few were armed with guns, some with bows, and others with war clubs.* They were painted in a manner that

---

* The bows are short, but strong. Those which are esteemed the best, are made of the horns of the animal called by the French *gros corne*. This animal inhabits the Rocky Mountains, and is gregarious. All who have seen it, represent its agility in leaping from rock to rock as one of the most surprising things they ever beheld. The Americans call it the mountain sheep ; but the probability is that it belongs to the genus antelope. The horns are exceedingly large for the size of the animal. The bows are made of three pieces, very neatly joined together by a long splice, and wound round with sinew in a very exact manner. The next in value, and but little inferior, are made of a yellow wood, from a tree which grows on Red River, and per-

seemed as if they had studied to make themselves hideous. Many of them had the mark which indicates that they had drank the blood of an enemy. This mark is made by rubbing the hand all over with vermillion, and by laying it on the mouth, it leaves a complete impression on the face, which is designed to resemble and indicate a bloody hand. With every band some scalps were carried, elevated on long sticks; but it was easy to perceive, on a close examination, that the scalps had been divided, to increase the apparent number. The number of the enemy that were killed we supposed did not exceed seven or eight, and they had themselves lost two, so that this engagement had not been a very bloody one. As the body approached the town, the squaws and old men began to meet them, and excepting the lamentations of those whose re-

---

haps on the Arkansas. This wood is called *bois jaune,* or *bois d'arc.* I do not think the tree has yet been described, unless it has been found lately in Mexico. I have seen two trees of this species in the garden of Pierre Chouteau, in St. Louis, and found that it belongs to the class *dioecia;* but both of the trees being females, I could not determine the genus. The fruit is as large as an apple, and is rough on the outside. It bleeds an acrid milky juice when wounded, and is called by the hunters the Osage orange. The price of a bow made from this wood at the Aricaras is a horse and a blanket. Many of the war clubs are made of the same kind of wood, and have the blade of a knife, or some sharp instrument, fastened at the end, and projecting from four to six inches, forming a right angle with the club.

latives had been killed or wounded, the expressions of joy became general, but without disturbing in the least the order of the procession. I walked into the village, which assumed a busy air. On the entrance of the party the warriors were conducted to the different lodges, that they might refresh themselves, and the old men went about shaking hands with some, and seemingly bestowing praises on others, who had conducted themselves well in the battle. As the time fixed on for the departure of Mr. Hunt and his party by land was now approaching, I quitted this scene of festivity, in order to resume my employment, and returned to the camp, where I found the party busily employed in preparing for their departure, by parching and grinding corn, mixing it with sugar, and putting it in bags. I now ascertained that the three men who had promised to accompany me down the river had changed their minds, and that on account of the now determined and inveterate hostility of the Sioux, they could not be prevailed on to venture, although I made them liberal offers. Two of them had determined to join the expedition : the other, Amos Richardson, was very anxious to descend the river, four years having elapsed since he had seen the house of a white man ; but he and myself would not have been sufficient to navigate the boat. Notwithstanding this I commenced to fill the caisettes with plants, and place them in my boat, and in the

evening again walked up to the village, where I
met Mr. Brackenridge, who had amused himself
during the afternoon by attending to the proceed-
ings consequent on the return of the war party., I
was also met by my friend the young warrior, who
invited me into his lodge, and repeated his request
that I would be his guest during my stay. I gave
him a few yards of printed calico and some
gunpowder. In return he pressed me to accept
a bow and a quiver full of arrows. Whilst we
were smoking his sister prepared some buffalo meat
with hominy, of which we ate, and after shaking
hands with him, I joined Mr. Brackenridge. In the
village all kinds of labour amongst the women was
suspended: the old men were going from lodge to
lodge, probably to enquire the particulars of the
engagement, and to bestow praises on those who
had behaved well. The tops and entrances of the
lodges were adorned with the shields and arms of
the warriors, and all seemed joy and festivity, with
the exception of the squaws who were mourning
the loss of the killed. It may not be amiss to observe that these people had more reason to rejoice
for this victory, than many European nations have
had for those of infinitely more importance in appearance. For although it had not been attended
with so much bloodshed as some battles in Europe
have, yet it had for the present driven away an
enemy, who had for two or three weeks been ho-

vering round, and threatened us all with starvation. This enemy is the oldest and most implacable they have, and has already succeeded so far in effecting their extermination, that they are reduced from composing ten large tribes to their present number. These miscreants have been constantly their oppressors, and rob and murder them sometimes with impunity. The present number which the two villages contain is estimated at 2000, and the warriors 500, but I think it overrated. They are derived from the Panies, and are stout and well built. The men go mostly naked in summer, and when disposed to make use of a covering, it consists of only a part of a buffalo skin thrown over the shoulders, with a hole for the right arm to pass through. This can be thrown off in an instant. They scarcely ever appear without arms beyond the limits of the town. As the nature of the country renders it necessary that they should pursue their game on horseback, frequent practice renders them not only good horsemen, but also teaches them to handle their bows, and strike an object with precision, when at full speed, with their arrows. They chiefly subsist on the buffalo, and when a herd is discovered, a considerable number of the hunters dispose themselves in such a manner as to approach as near as possible unperceived by them. This must always be done with due regard to the direction of the wind, on account of the exquisite de-

gree in which this animal possesses the sense of
smelling. The instant they are perceived by the
herd, they dash in amongst them, each singling out
one. The horse is taught to understand and obey
the wishes of his rider, although conveyed to him
by the slightest movement. When he has overtaken a buffalo, he does not offer to pass it, but continues at an even pace until the arrow is discharged,
when the rider singles out another immediately, if
he thinks the first arrow has effected his purpose.
If the horse has sufficient strength and wind to enable his rider to kill three buffaloes, he is held in
great estimation. None of these would be sold by
the Aricaras to Mr. Hunt. After the horses are
out of breath, they pursue the wounded animals at
leisure, as they separate from the herd on being
wounded, and are soon left behind from weakness,
occasioned by loss of blood. To produce a more
copious discharge, the heads of the arrows designed
to be used in hunting are much broader than those
intended for war. The heads of both are flat, and
of the form of an isosceles triangle ; the length of
the two equal sides three times that of the base.*
In neither does the shaft of the arrow fill up the

---

* Before the Indians had any intercourse with the whites,
they made the heads of their arrows of flint or horn stone. They
now purchase them from the traders, who cut them from rolled
iron or from hoops.

wound which the head has made ; but the shaft of
the hunting arrow is fluted, to promote a still greater discharge of blood. On these occasions they often
kill many more than they can possibly dispose of,
and it has already been observed that hunting parties are frequently followed by wolves, who profit
by this wanton destruction.

The Aricaras do not provide any better for their
horses than the other nations of the Missouri.
They cut down the cotton wood, *(Populus angulosa)* and the horses feed on the bark and smaller
branches. I have seen instances exhibiting proofs
that these poor animals have eaten branches two
inches in diameter. The women, as is the custom
with Indians, do all the drudgery, and are excellent
cultivators. I have not seen, even in the United States,
any crop of Indian corn in finer order, or better
managed than the corn about these villages. They
also cultivate squashes, beans, and the small species
of tobacco *(Nicotiana rustica.)* The only implement of husbandry used by them is the hoe. Of
these they were so destitute before our arrival, that
I saw several of the squaws hoeing their corn with
the blade bone of a buffalo, ingeniously fixed in a
stick for that purpose.

I am not acquainted with any customs peculiar
to this nation, save that of having a sacred lodge

in the centre of the largest village. This is called
the *Medicine lodge,* and in one particular, corresponds with the sanctuary of the Jews, as no blood
is on any account whatsoever to be spilled within
it, not even that of an enemy; nor is any one,
having taken refuge there, to be forced from it.
This lodge is also the general place of deposit for
such things as they devote to the *Father of life.*
It does not seem absolutely necessary that every
thing devoted shall be deposited here :—one of
the chiefs, availing himself of this regulation, devoted his horse, or in their mode of expressing it,
" Gave it to his medicine," after which he could
not, according to their rules, give him away. This
exempted him, in respect to that particular object,
from the tax which custom lays on the chiefs of
this and most other nations. This will be explained by stating that generosity, or rather an indifference for self, forms here a necessary qualifi-
cation in a chief. The desire to acquire and possess more than others, is thought a passion too ig-
noble for a *brave man;* it often happens, therefore, that a chief is the poorest man in the com-
munity.

In respect to their general policy as regards
property, they seem to have correct ideas of the
meum and *tuum* amongst themselves; and when
the generally thievish character of those we call

savages is considered, the Indians of the Missouri are superlatively honest towards strangers. I never heard of a single instance of a white man being robbed, or having any thing stolen from him in an Indian villàge. It is true, that when they find white men trapping for beaver on the grounds which they claim, they often take from them the furs they have collected, and beat them severely with their *wiping sticks ;* but so far is this from being surprising, that it is a wonder they do not kill them, or take away their rifles.

The chief part of their riches consists in horses, many of which are obtained from the nations south west of them, as the Chayennes, Poncars, Panies, &c. who make predatory excursions into Mexico, and steal horses from the Spaniards. A considerable number of those bought from the Aricaras were branded, and were doubtless brought from Mexico, as the Indians do not practice branding.

There is nothing relative to the Indians so difficult to understand as their religion. They believe in a Supreme Being, in a future state, and in supernatural agency. Of the Great Spirit they do not pretend to give any account, but believe him to be the author and giver of all good. They believe in bad spirits, but seem to consider them rather as little wicked beings, who can only gratify their

malignity by driving away the game, preventing
the efficacy of medicine, or such petty mischief.
The belief in a future state seems to be general,
as it extends even to the Nodowessies or Sioux,
who are the furthest removed from civilization,
and who do not even cultivate the soil. It is
known, that frequently when an Indian has shot
down his enemy, and is preparing to scalp him,
with the tomahawk uplifted to give the fatal stroke,
he will address him in words to this effect, " My
name is Cashegra. I am a famous warrior, and
am now going to kill you. When you arrive at the
land of spirits, you will see the ghost of my father,
tell him it was Cashegra that sent you there." He
then gives the blow.

In respect to laws, I could never find that any
code is established, or that any crime against society becomes a subject of enquiry amongst the
chiefs, excepting cowardice or murder. The last
is, for the most part, punished with death, and the
nearest of kin is deputed by the council to act the
part of executioner. In some tribes, I am told,
this crime may be commuted. It scarcely requires to be observed, that chastity in females is
not a virtue, nor that a deviation from it is considered a crime, when sanctioned by the consent of
their husbands, fathers, or brothers: but in some
tribes, as the Potowatomies, Saukies, Foxes, &c.

the breach of it, without the consent of the husband, is punished severely, as he may bite off the nose of his squaw if she is found guilty.

No people on earth discharge the duties of hospitality with more cordial good-will than the Indians. On entering a lodge I was always met by the master, who first shook hands with me, and immediately looked for his pipe: before he had time to light it, a bear-skin, or that of a buffalo, was spread for me to sit on, although they sat on the bare ground. When the pipe was lighted, he smoked a few whiffs, and then handed it to me; after which it went round to all the men in the lodge. Whilst this was going on, the squaw prepared something to eat, which, when ready, was placed before me on the ground. The squaw, in some instances, examined my dress, and in particular my mockassons; if any repair was wanting, she brought a small leather bag, in which she kept her awls and split sinew, and put it to rights. After conversing as well as we could by signs, if it was near night, I was made to understand that a bed was at my service; in general this offer was accompanied also by that of a *bedfellow*.

The two men, Jones and Carson, whom we met descending the Missouri on the 22nd of May, had remained with the Aricaras during the winter, and

M

on our return, Carson was desirous of rewarding
the Indian with whom he had boarded during that
period. For that purpose he obtained some articles
from Mr. Hunt, and offered them to the *savage,*
who refused to accept them, and as a reason for it
observed that " *Carson was poorer than himself.*

I breakfasted with Mr. Lisa the day following,
and found that he intended to send two of the
boats purchased from Mr. Hunt to St. Louis, with
skins and furs, and that Mr. Brackenridge purposed to descend with them. I knew also that in a
week our party would take their departure for the
Pacific Ocean. Messrs. Hunt, Crooks, and M'Kenzie invited me to go to the Pacific, and in the first
instance I was inclined to accept the invitation;
but finding that they could not assure me of a passage from thence to the United States by sea, or
even to China, and recollecting also that I must
sacrifice my present collection by adopting that
measure, and that in passing over the Rocky Mountains, I should probably be unable to preserve or
carry my specimens, I declined. There was now
something of uncertainty whether Mr. Lisa would
return to St. Louis in autumn, or remain during
the winter.

On duly weighing all these circumstances, I resolved to return in the boats which were intended

to be dispatched down the river, although it did not exactly suit my views, as I had noticed a great number of species of plants on the river that, from the early state of the season, could not then be collected advantageously. These I had reserved for my descent ; but as no man would accompany me but Richardson, I applied to Mr. Lisa, informing him of my wish to descend in his boats, and on consideration of being permitted to land at certain places which I pointed out, I offered to give him my boat as an equivalent. To this he readily agreed, and I continued to prepare for my departure.

It had been a matter of surprise to me on my return from Fort Mandan, to find plenty of fresh buffalo meat in our camp, as the fear of the Sioux had not yet subsided. On enquiry I found that Mr. Hunt had hit upon an expedient which proved successful. This was to dispatch a boat up the river in the night to some miles distant, affording by that means an opportunity to the hunters. This boat returned with a plentiful supply, and secured the party from starving, as a considerable portion of the Indian dogs were already consumed. I was not less surprised on learning that at least two-thirds of our Canadians had experienced unpleasant consequences from their intercourse with the squaws, notwithstanding which, the traffic mentioned before continued. I had been informed by Jones and Carson of the existence of this evil, but found it was of the mildest description, and that here, where no spirituous liquors or salt is used, they do not fear it. I found some of the Canadians digging up roots, with which I understood they made a decoction, and used it as a drink. They mostly preferred the roots of *Rudbeckia purpurea*, and sometimes they used those of *Houstonia longifolia*.

This morning a circumstance came to our knowledge, that gave serious alarm to Mr. Hunt and the leaders of the party. During the night a cask of gunpowder belonging to me had been stolen from amongst the baggage, and from the security of our situation, and the precautions we had taken, it was impossible the Indians could have stolen it. Our camp was situated immediately on the bank of the river; the tents, together with the men sleeping in their blankets, surrounded the baggage, and four men were constantly on guard during the night, walking round the camp in sight of each other. I had been on guard in the fore part of the night, and Mr. Crooks on the latter watch. No collusion could therefore be suspected. Other circumstances also concurred in producing a belief that some of the party intended to desert, and on examination I found that one of my trunks had been opened, and a pistol, some flints, my belt, and a few shirts,

taken out. In confirmation of our opinions, John
Day, one of the hunters, informed Mr. Hunt of
his having overheard some of the Canadians mur-
muring at the fatigues they had already undergone,
and expressing an opinion that they should all be
murdered, in the journey they were going to undertake. The safety of the party depended, in a
great measure, on its strength; a diminution in
the number, if considerable, might therefore
defeat the enterprize; a search was made in all
the neighbourhood of the camp, and even in the
bank of the river, but without effect. As my boat
might facilitate a desertion, I caused it to be removed to Mr. Lisa's camp, who moored it in safety
with his own boats; and I employed myself, for
the remainder of the day, in filling the boxes.

On account of my constant attention to plants,
and being regularly employed in collecting, I was
considered as the physician of the party by all the
nations we saw; and generally the *medicine men*
amongst them sought my acquaintance. This day,
the doctor, whom Mr. Brackenridge and myself
saw in the upper village, and who showed me his
medicine bag, came to examine my plants. I
found he understood a few French words, such as
bon, mal, &c. I presented him with some small
ornaments of silver, with which he appeared to be
very much pleased, and requested of me that I

would go to his lodge, and smoke with him. When I entered, he spread a fine new buffaloe robe for me to sit on, and showed me that it was a present, which he wished me to accept. I smoked with him, and regretted much that we could only converse by signs, and he seemed also to feel the same regret. He showed me a quantity of a plant lately gathered, and by signs informed me that it cured the cholic. It was a new species of *Amorpha*. I returned to the camp, accompanied by the doctor, who very politely carried the buffaloe robe for me.

On the 17th I took leave of my worthy friends, Messrs. Hunt, Crooks, and M'Kenzie, whose kindness and attention to me had been such as to render the parting painful; and I am happy in having this opportunity of testifying my gratitude and respect for them: throughout the whole voyage, every indulgence was given me, that was consistent with their duty, and the general safety. Mr. Lisa had loaded two boats with skins and furs, in each of which were six men. Mr. Brackenridge, Amos Richardson, and myself were passengers. On passing our camp, Mr. Hunt caused the men to draw up in a line, and give three cheers, which we returned; and we soon lost sight of them, as we moved at the rate of about nine miles per hour. I now found, to my great surprise, that Mr. Lisa had instructed Mr. Brackenridge not, on any account, to stop in the day, but if possible, to go night and day. As this measure would deprive me of all hopes of adding to my collection any of the plants lower down on the river, and was directly contrary to our agreement, I was greatly mortified and chagrined; and although I found that Mr. Brackenridge felt sensibly for my disappointment, yet I could not expect that he would act contrary to the directions given by Lisa, and had the mortification during the day, of passing a number of plants that may probably remain unknown for ages.

Our descent was very rapid, and the day remarkably fine; we had an opportunity, therefore, of considering the river more in its *tout ensemble* than in our ascent, and the changes of scenery came upon us with a succession so quick, as to keep the eye and the mind continually employed. We soon came in sight of the bluffs which border the Chayenne river, stretching as far as the eye could reach, and visible only through the low intervals in those bordering the Missouri. Before night we passed the Chayenne, and during a few moments had a view of its stream, for two or three miles above its junction with the Missouri. It is one of the largest rivers that falls into it, being at least 400 yards wide at its mouth, and navigable to a great distance. The banks appear to be more steep than those of the Missouri, and are clothed with trees to the water's edge. On both sides of the river we saw numberless herds of buffaloe, grazing in tranquillity, some of them not a quarter of a mile from us when we passed them. We continued under way until late in the evening, and encamped on an island ; a measure we determined to pursue when practicable, as we knew that to fall into the hands of the Sioux would be certain death.

18th.—We set out early, and continued under way during the whole of the day without interruption, and encamped on Great Cedar Island, where a French trader, named L'Oiselle, formerly had a post or trading house. This island is about two miles in length, and mostly covered with very fine cedar, and some rose and currant bushes, considerably overrun with vines, on which some of the grapes were already changing colour.

19th.—In the early part of the day we arrived at the upper part of the Great Bend, and continued to see innumerable herds of buffaloes on both sides of the river. I now found that although our *patron*, or steersman, who conducted the first boat, and directed our motions, was determined to obey strictly the orders of Lisa as regarded expedition, yet from his timidity I had some hope of opportunities to collect.

Before we entirely passed the Great Bend a breeze arose, which ruffled the surface of the river : He put ashore, not daring to proceed, and we lay to during the remainder of the day, having descended about 280 miles in about two days and a half. I determined not to lose this opportunity to add a few species to my collection, and was accompanied in my excursion by Mr. Brackenridge, who employed himself in keeping a good look out for fear of a surprise by the Sioux, a precaution necessary to my safety, as the nature of my employment kept me for the most part in a stooping posture. The track of land which is inclosed in the Bend proba · bly contains about forty square miles, nearly level, and the soil excellent. It was at this time covered with fine grass, with scattered groves of trees, betwixt which many herds of buffaloes were quietly grazing : we did not wish to disturb them, for fear of thereby enabling the Sioux to discover us.

20th.—About nine o'clock we discovered some buffaloes grazing near the edge of the river, about half a mile below us, and in such a position that we might apparently approach very near them without being discovered. We landed a little above them, and approached within about sixty yards, when four of the party fired. It appeared that two were wounded, one of which fled towards the river, into which it plunged, and was immediately pursued by one of the boats, whilst the party ashore followed the other, among whom I ran, but I was much less intent on obtaining the buffalo, than on procuring some plants which I knew were to be had on the bluffs, and actually succeeded. In about half an hour the party gave up the pursuit, being unsuccessful, and returned discouraged to the place where they had left me. But as I had not gone over the bluffs, and had observed what had passed in the river, I gave them the pleasing intelligence that the boat had overtaken the other buffalo, and that the men were now employed in dragging the carcass ashore. We soon joined them, and in a few minutes the animal was skinned and cut up. It was by much the fattest we had seen, and the tallow it contained was very considerable.*

We soon passed White River, which is inferior both in magnitude and beauty to the Chienne, if we may judge from its mouth, where it is not more than 300 yards wide. Soon after we passed the river,

---

* I am informed by the hunters, that in autumn the quantity of tallow or fat in the buffalo is very great. It of course begins to diminish when food becomes scarce. As the same thing obtains in a number of animals, by climate and habit ordained to procure abundance of food in summer, and to suffer great privation in winter, this collection of fat seems to be a kind of reservoir, containing the means of existence, which is drained by absorbent vessels, and returned into the system when necessary.

we saw a buffalo running over the bluff towards the Missouri, which put us on our guard, as we considered it a certain indication of Indians being near. Immediately below the river the vast vein of iron ore commences which has been before mentioned. I again noticed its exact conformity on both sides of the river, in point of elevation and thickness of the vein.

As the evening approached we noticed a succession of flashes of lightning, just appearing over the bluffs, on the opposite side of the river. This did not for some time excite much attention, as it was by no means an uncommon occurrence; but we soon began to apprehend impending danger, as we perceived that the storm advanced with great rapidity, accompanied with appearances truly terrific. The cloud was of a pitchy blackness, and so dense as to resemble a solid body, out of which, at short intervals, the lightning poured in a stream of one or two seconds in duration. It was too late to cross the river, and unfortunately for us, the side on which we were was entirely bounded by rocks. We looked most anxiously for some little harbour, or jutting point, behind which we might shelter ourselves; but not one appeared, and darkness came on with a rapidity I never before witnessed. It was not long that any choice was left us. We plainly heard the storm coming. We stopped and fastened our boats to some shrubs, *(Amorpha fruticosa)* which grew in abundance out of the clefts of these rocks, and prepared to save ourselves and our little barks if possible. At each end of the boats there was a small deck : under these we stowed our provisions, &c.: next to the decks were piled the packs of skins, secured by ropes, and in the middle a space of about twelve feet long was left for the oarsmen. Fortunately for us we had some broad boards in each boat, designed as a defence against arrows, had we been attacked by the Sioux. These boards we placed on the gunwale of the boats, and crammed our blankets into such parts as the lightning enabled us at intervals to see did not fit closely. Before we had time to lash our boards the gale commenced, and in a few minutes the swell was tremendous. For nearly an hour it required the utmost exertion of our strength to hold the boards to their places, and before the storm abated we were nearly exhausted, as also were those who were occupied in baling. As the river is in this place nearly a mile in breadth, and being on the lee shore, the waves were of considerable magnitude, and frequently broke over the boats. Had our fastenings given way, we must inevitably have perished. When the wind abated the rain increased, and continued for the greater part of the night, during which my friend Brackenridge and myself lay on the deck, rolled up in our wet blankets, congratulating ourselves on our escape. For myself I felt but little : two years in a great measure spent in the wilds, had inured me to hardships and inclemencies ; but I felt much for my friend Brackenridge. *Poor young man*, his youth, and the delicacy of his frame, ill suited him for such hardships, which, nevertheless, he supported cheerfully.

In the morning the sun rose unobscured, which was to us extremely welcome, as its heat soon rendered us comparatively comfortable. We passed the river L'Eau qui Court, and shortly afterwards the place where we met the Poncar Indians, and as the wind began to blow fresh, we stopped five or six miles lower down, nearly at the place where I met the three Indians on the 24th of May. This enabled me to procure roots of the new species of currant, although with much pain and difficulty, having four miles at least to wade through water and mud, as the river had recently overflowed its banks. On my return to the boats, as the wind had in some degree abated, we proceeded, and had not gone more than five or six miles before we were surprised by a dull hollow sound, the cause of which we could not possibly imagine. It seemed to be one or two miles below us ; but as our descent was very rapid, it increased every moment in loudness, and before we had proceeded far, our ears were able to catch some distinct tones, indicating the bellowing of buffaloes. When opposite to the place from whence it proceeded, we landed, ascended the bank, and entered a small skirting of trees and shrubs, that separated the river from an extensive plain. On gaining a view of it, such a scene opened to us as will fall to the lot of few travellers to witness. This plain was literally covered with buffaloes as far as we could see, and we soon discovered that it consisted in part of females. The males were fighting in every direction, with a fury which I have never seen paralleled, each having singled out his antagonist. We judged that the number must have amounted to some thousands, and that there were many hundreds of these battles going on at the same time, some not eighty yards from us. It will be recollected that at this season the females would naturally admit the society of the males. From attentively observing some of the combats nearest to us, I am persuaded that our domestic bull would almost invariably be worsted in a contest with this animal, as he is inferior to him both in strength and ferocity. A shot was fired amongst them, which they seemed not to notice. Mr. Brackenridge joined me in preventing a volley being-fired, as it would have been useless, and therefore wanton; for if we had killed one, I am certain the weight of his carcass in gold would not have bribed us to fetch him. I shall only observe farther, that the noise occasioned by the trampling and bellowing was far beyond description. In the evening, before we e camped, another immense herd made its appearance, running along the bluffs at full speed, and although at least a mile from us, we could distinctly hear the sound of their feet, which resembled distant thunder.

The morning of the next day was very fine : we saw some buffaloe swimming, at which the men fired, contrary to our wishes, as we did not intend to stop for them. The stream was very rapid : we passed the Sulphur bluffs, and stopped a short time at Floyd's grave. Shortly afterwards we arrived at the trading house opposite the Maha village, but saw no one, nor did we wish it, as Mr. Lisa had not called on the Big Elk when he ascended, who might probably be offended at his neglect. We encamped on some drift wood from necessity, not being able to get ashore. The navigation of the river had now become much more difficult, and we had in the two succeeding days some very narrow escapes. The river was much higher than at any former period, and from the Mahas to the River Platte, is more crooked than in any other part. At every sudden turn the momentum of the boats had a continual tendency to throw them ashore on the outer bank, which it required all the skill of the steersman, and strength of the oarsmen, to prevent.

In two instances we were very near being carried into the woods, in places where the river overflowed its banks. We arrived at Fort Osage, now Fort Clark on the 27th in the afternoon, and were very politely received by Major Brownson. I had the pleasure to find that Mr. Sibly had returned a few days before from his tour to the Arkansas, to examine the vast body of salt in the neighbourhood of that river. He very politely furnished us with extracts from his journal, which are as follow :—

" After giving a number of medals to the Panie chiefs, and having various counsels with them, I left their villages on the 4th of June, and proceeded to the Little Osage Camp, on the Arkansas, about seventy-five miles south, and sixteen east from the Panies, where I safely arrived on the 11th. I remained several days with the Osages, who had abundance of provisions, they having killed two hundred buffaloes within a few days. Where they had their camp, the Arkansas was about 200 yards wide, the water shallow, rapid, and of a red colour. On the 16th the Indians raised their camp, and proceeded towards the hilly country, on the other side of the Arkansas. I continued with them about fifty miles west and thirty miles east, when we fell in with some men of the Chaniers Band, who informed us that their camp was at no great distance, and the camp of the Big Osage still nearer. In consequence, I determined to pass through both on my way to the Grand Salines. On the 21st I rode south forty miles, east thirty, to the Big Osage camp; nearly all the warriors were at war, or abroad hunting. I was remarkably well treated by young White Hair and family; I however remained but one night with them. On the 22d I rode twenty miles south, fifteen east, to the Chanier's camp, where we arrived about one o'clock. We were well treated by the head men; and indeed, this is one of the tribes most attached to the Americans. The chief's name is Clermont. From hence is forty miles to the Grand Salines, which we reached early on the morning of the 24th. I hasten to give you a description of this celebrated curiosity.

The Grand Saline is situated about two hundred and eighty miles south-west of Fort Osage, between two forks of a small branch of the Arkansas, one of which washes its southern extremity; and the other, the principal one, runs nearly parallel, within a mile of its opposite side. It is a hard level plain, of reddish coloured sand, and of an irregular or mixed figure. Its greatest length is from north-west to south-east, and its circumference full thirty miles. From the appearance of drift-wood that is scattered over, it would seem that the whole plain is at times inundated by the overflowing of the streams that pass near it. This plain is entirely covered in hot dry weather, from two to six inches deep, with a crust of beautiful clean white salt, of a quality rather superior to the imported blown salt : it bears a striking resemblance to a field of brilliant snow after a rain, with a light crust on its top. On a bright sunny morning, the appearance of this natural curiosity is highly picturesque : it possesses the quality of looming, or magnifying objects, and this in a very striking degree, making the small billets of wood appear as formidable as trees. Numbers of buffaloe were on the plain. The Saline is environed by a stripe of marshy prairie, with a few scattered trees, mostly of cotton wood ; behind these is a range of sand hills, some of which are perfectly naked, others thinly clothed with verdure and dwarf plum bushes, not more than thirty inches in height, from which we procured abundance of the most delicious plums I ever tasted. The distance to a navigable branch of the Arkansas is about eighty miles, the country tolerably level, and the water courses easily passed. About sixty miles south-west of this, I came to the Saline, the whole of this distance lying over a country remarkably rugged and broken, affording the most romantic and picturesque views imaginable. It is a tract of about seventy-five miles square, in which nature has displayed a great variety of the most strange and whimsical vagaries. It is an assemblage of beautiful meadows, verdant ridges, and rude, mis-shapen piles of red clay, thrown together in the utmost apparent confusion, yét affording the most pleasing harmonies, and presenting us in every direction an endless variety of curious and interesting objects. After winding along for a few miles on the high ridges, you suddenly descend an almost perpendicular declivity of rocks and clay, into a series of level, fertile meadows, watered by some beautiful rivulets, and here and there adorned with shrubby cotton wood trees, elms, and cedars. These meadows are divided by chains formed of red clay, and huge masses of gypsum, with here and there a pyramid of gravel; one might imagine himself surrounded by the ruins of some ancient city, and that the plain had sunk, by some convulsion of nature, more than one hundred feet below its former level; for some of the huge columns of red clay rise to the height of two hundred feet perpendicular, capped with rocks of gypsum, which the hand of time is ever crumbling off, and strewing in beautiful transparent flakes along the declivities of the hills, glittering like so many mirrors in the sun."

Mr. Sibly also showed me a letter from his father, Dr. Sibly of Natchitoches, informing him of a mass of native iron having been brought down the Red River, which weighed about 2500 pounds. In the fort we saw the young bears which we gave them in passing up the river; they had grown surprisingly, and were quite tame, excepting whilst feeding, when all bears are more fierce than at other times.

28th.—After breakfasting at the fort, we set off, and encamped near where Fort Orleans formerly was situated.

29th.—About noon we came in sight of a white man's house, at Boon's Lick, and our boatmen immediately set up a shout. Soon after, some men appeared at the edge of a field of Indian corn, close to the river: they invited us ashore, and we willingly complied. In passing through the corn, I was much struck with its luxuriance: I judged it not to be less than fourteen feet high, and the ears were far above my head. It was Sunday, and when we arrived at the house, we found three women there, all dressed in clean white gowns, and being in other respects very neat; they formed a pleasing contrast to the squaws whom we had of late been in the habit of seeing. They soon spread the table for us, and produced bread, milk, and preserved fruits, which I thought the most delicious that I ever tasted. We arrived at St. Louis in safety, where I had the pleasure of shaking hands with my worthy friend, Mr. Abraham Gallatin, at whose house I slept. Early the next day, I called at the post office, and found letters from England, informing me of the welfare of my family. This pleasing intelligence was damped by a letter from my son, who informed me that those who had agreed to furnish me with the means of prosecuting my tour, and to whom I had sent my former collection, had determined to withhold any further supply. Early in the forenoon, my worthy and respected friend, Mr. S. Bridge, from Manchester, came to St. Louis, and invited me to take up my residence for the present with him; I learned from him that during my absence he had bought a considerable quantity of land, on which he had built a house. He sent his waggon for my plants, and allotted me a piece of ground, which, with much labour, I prepared in a few days, got it surrounded by a fence, and transplanted the whole of my collection. I found the situation of Mr. Bridge's house extremely pleasant, and his plantation of the first quality of land. Within 150 yards of his house, was a small vein of coal, from twelve to eighteen inches in thickness, and rising to the surface. For this land he had paid one dollar, sixty-five cents per arpent, or French acre.*

---

* The arpent is to the statute acre nearly in the proportion of 83 to 100.

In about ten days after my arrival I was attacked by a bilious fever, which confined me to my bed. Its violence soon left me little hope of recovery. In about a month it became intermittent, and continued until the beginning of December.

During my illness a circumstance occurred, a relation of which will tend to show the almost unconquerable attachment to the hunting life in those accustomed to it. It will be remembered that a man named Richardson accompanied us down the Missouri, and that it has been related of him that he had been several years in the wilderness. He had there suffered more than common hardships, having been often ill treated by the Indians, and once severely wounded by an arrow. This man, during our descent, seemed to look forward with great anxiety to the time when we should arrive in the settlements, and often declared his intention never again to adopt the hunting life. When I had been sick about three weeks, he came to see me, and after some conversation, reminded me of my having mentioned a design to ascend the Arkansas River, and requested that I would admit him as my companion, if I persisted in my intention. I spoke of my doubts whether I should ever recover, and expressed my surprise at so sudden a change in his intentions. He replied, " I find so much deceit and selfishness amongst white men, that

I am already tired of them. The arrow head which is not yet extracted pains me when I chop wood, whiskey I can't drink, and bread and salt I don't care about: I will go again amongst the Indians."

Towards the latter end of November I received a remittance from those who had determined to withhold it, together with a letter from the person* who managed the Botanic Garden at Liverpool, informing me that he had received my former collection, out of which he had secured in pots more than one thousand plants, and that the seeds were already vegetating in vast numbers. As I had now so far recovered as to be able to ride to St. Louis, I visited my friend Mr. Gallatin, and remained with him some days, during which I often saw a young gentleman from Philadelphia, Mr. H. W. Drinker, who had frequently called to see me in my sickness, and whose talents and amiable manners had created in me a strong attachment to him. In a tour through the country west of the Alleghanies, he visited St. Louis, and pleased with the beauty of the place, had resided there for some months. Finding that I was determined to descend the Mississippi to New Orleans, he invited me to take my passage with him, as he purposed to take a boat down to that place, loaded with lead, of

---

* This man's name is Shepherd.

which he had a sufficient quantity. This was a very favourable opportunity, and I made every exertion my weak state would admit of, to be in readiness. A short time afterwards Mr. Drinker as-certained that some debts due to him, and contracted to be paid in lead, could not be collected until the ensuing spring : he therefore found himself neces-sitated to remain at St. Louis until that period. But aware of the impossibility of my detaining what yet remained of my collection till that season, he offered to buy a boat, load it with lead, and com-mit it to my care, with liberty to sell the lead at Orleans, or store it for his account. This kind and generous offer I gladly accepted, and in a few days a boat was procured, and her cargo put on board, amounting to about 30,000 lbs. of lead. Her crew consisted of five French Creoles, four of whom were oarsmen, and the fifth steered the boat, he is call-ed the *patron*.

On the evening of the 4th of December we were in perfect readiness, and I took leave of my friends at St. Louis, several of whom, from their polite attention to me, I have reason to hold in lasting remembrance ; and in addition to those I have already mentioned, I ought not to omit Mr. Josh. Charless, editor of the Missouri Gazette, whose disposition and manners gain him the esteem of all who know him : mine he will always retain. It has been omitted to state, that in November Mr. Lisa arrived at St. Louis, and delivered to me a letter from Mr. Hunt, who informed me, that after my departure from the Aricaras, whilst the men were still assembled to watch our boats descend, he addressed them on the subject of my cask of powder, which was stolen, and with such effect, that one of the Canadians came privately to his tent the night following, and informed him where it was buried in the bank of the river. Mr. Hunt caused a search to be made the day after, and found it. As Mr. Lisa was in want of powder, he bought it, and paid me for it on his return.

On the 5th of December I set off from St. Louis on the voyage to New Orleans, a distance of about 1350 miles. I was accompanied by Mr. John Bridge, who I admitted as a passenger at the request of his brother. He purposed to sail from Orleans to the eastern states. We arrived at St. Genevieve in the evening, and slept at the mouth of Gabarie, a small creek near the village, where boats trading to that place usually stop. Having some business to transact at St. Genevieve, I was detained until the afternoon of the following day. During my stay here, I became acquainted with a gentleman of the name of Longprie, a native of St. Domingo. He had a boat in part loaded with lead, intended for Orleans. It was much wished by both of us that we should descend in company, as, in case of an accident happening to one, assistance might be rendered by the other ; but as he could not be ready in less than two days, I set out, intending to travel leisurely, that he might be enabled to overtake me. It may be necessary to remark in this place, that the navigation of the Mississippi is attended with considerable danger, and in particular to boats loaded with lead. These, by reason of the small space occupied by the cargo, in case of striking against a *planter* or a *sawyer*, sink instantly. That these terms may be understood, it must be observed that the alluvion of the Mississippi is almost in every part covered with timber close to the edge of the river, and that in some part or other encroachments are continually made, and in particular during the time of the floods, when it often happens that tracts of some acres in extent are carried away in a few days. As in most instances a large body of earth is attached to the roots of the trees, it sinks that part to the bottom of the river, whilst the upper part, more buoyant, rises to the surface in an inclined posture, generally with the head of the tree pointing down the river. Some of these are firmly fixed and immoveable, and are therefore termed *planters*. Others, although they do not remove from where they are placed, are constantly in motion, the whole tree is sometimes entirely submerged by the pressure of the stream, and carried to a greater depth by its momentum than the stream can maintain. On rising, its momentum in the other direction causes many of its huge limbs to be lifted above the surface of the the river. The period of this oscillatory motion is sometimes of several minutes duration. These are the *sawyers*, and are much more dangerous than the *planters*, as no care or caution can guard sufficiently against them. The steersman this instant sees all the surface of the river smooth and tranquil, and the next he is struck with horror on seeing just before him the *sawyer* raising his terrific arms, and so near that neither strength nor skill can save him from destruction. This is not figurative : many boats have been lost in this way, and more particularly those descending. From these and other risks, it is common for those carrying lead to have a canoe with them, in which they may save themselves in case of any accident happening to the boat.

Until the 14th, no occurrence happened worth noticing, excepting that we saw on the bank of the river four Indians, who beckoned to us, and we accordingly landed near them, and found they were Choctaws, who wanted to sell some venison and some turkies. As they were acquainted with the use of money, I bought from them three turkies and two hind quarters of venison for three quarters of a dollar, being what they asked.

On the 14th in the evening, we arrived at New Madrid, and having occasion for some necessaries, I bought them in the morning. I was much disappointed in this place, as I found only a few straggling houses, situated round a plain of 'from two to three hundred acres in extent. There are only two stores, and those very indifferently furnished. We set off about nine o'clock, and passed the Upper Chickasaw Bluffs; these bluffs are of soft sand-stone rock, of a yellow colour, but some parts being highly charged with oxyd of iron, the whole has a clouded appearance, and is considered as a curiosity by the boatmen. At the lower end of the bluffs we saw a smoke, and on a nearer approach, observed five or six Indians, and on the opposite side of the river, but lower down, we heard a dog howling. When the Indians perceived us, they held up some venison, to show us that they wished to dispose of it. Being desirous of adding to our stock of fresh meat, I hastily got into the canoe, and took with me one of the men, named La France, who spoke the Chickasaw language, as I supposed the Indians to be of that nation. We very imprudently went without arms, an omission that gave me some uneasiness before we reached them; especially as the boat, by my direction, proceeded leisurely on.

We found the Indians had plenty of deer's

flesh, and some turkies. I began to bargain for
them, when the people in the boat fired a shot,
and the dog on the other side of the river instantly ceased to howl. The Indians immediately flew to their arms, speaking all together,
with much earnestness. La France appeared
much terrified, and told me that they said our
people in the boat had shot their dog. I desired
him to tell them that we did not believe that
our people had shot their dog, but if they had,
I would pay them any price for him. They
seemed too much infuriated to hearken to him, and
surrounded us, with their weapons in their hands.
They were very clamorous amongst themselves,
and as I was afterwards told by La France, could not
agree whether they should immediately put us to
death, or keep us prisoners until we could procure
goods from the boat to pay for the dog, on which it
appeared they set a high value. Most fortunately
for us, the dog, at this instant began to bark opposite
to us, having run a considerable distance up the
river after the shot was fired. The tomahawks
were immediately laid aside, and I bargained for
half a deer, for which I gave them a quarter dollar and some gunpowder. I was not very exact in
measuring the last, being rather anxious to get
away, and could perceive that La France had no
desire to stay any longer.

On reaching our canoe we seized our paddles, and being told by La France that we were not yet out of danger, I joined him in making every exertion to get out of their reach. When we conceived ourselves safe, we relaxed, and he told me that even when we were leaving them, they were deliberating whether they should detain us or not; some of them having remarked that the dog might be wounded. We had been so long delayed by this adventure, that it was more than an hour before we overtook the boat. I blamed them much for firing, and charged them with having fired at the dog: this, however, appeared not to have been the case, as they had fired at a loon, (*Mergus merganser.*) In the course of this day, we passed no fewer than thirteen arks, or Kentucky boats, going with produce to Orleans; all these we left a considerable distance behind, as they only float with the stream, and we made considerable head way with our oars. In the evening we came in view of a dangerous part of the river called by the Americans the *Devil's Channel,* and by the French *Chenal du Diable.* It appears to be caused by a bank that crosses the river in this place, and renders, it shallow. On this bank, a great number of trees have lodged; and on account of the shallowness of the river, a considerable portion of the branches are raised above the surface; through these the water rushes with such impetuosity as to be heard at the distance of some miles.

As it required every effort of skill and exertion to pass through this channel in safety, and as the sun had set, I resolved to wait until the morning, and caused the boat to be moored to a small island, about 500 yards above the entrance into the channel. After supper, we went to sleep as usual: about ten o'clock, and in the night I was awakened by a most tremendous noise, accompanied by an agitation of the boat so violent, that it appeared in danger of upsetting. Before I could quit the bed, or rather the skin, upon which I lay, the four men who slept in the other cabin rushed in and cried out in the greatest terror, *" O mon Dieu! Monsieur Bradbury, qu'est ce ? qu'il y a?"* I passed them with some difficulty, and ran to the door of the cabin, where I could distinctly see the river as if agitated by a storm ; and although the noise was inconceivably loud and terrific, I could distinctly hear the crash of falling trees, and the screaming of the wild fowl on the river, but found that the boat was still safe at her moorings. I was followed out by the men and the *patron*, still in accents of terror, enquiring what it was : I tried to calm them by saying, *" Restez vous tranquil, c'est un tremblement de terre,"* which they did not seem to understand.

By the time we could get to our fire, which was on a large flag, in the stern of the boat, the shock had ceased; but immediately the perpendicular banks, both above and below us, began to fall into the river in such vast masses, as nearly to sink our boat by the swell they occasioned; and our *patron*, who seemed more terrified even than the men, began to cry out, " *O mon Dieu! nous perirons !* I wished to consult with him as to what we could do to preserve ourselves and the boat, but could get no answer except " *O mon Dieu! nous perirons!*" and "*Allons à terre! Allons à terre!*" As I found Mr. Bridge the only one who seemed to have retained any presence of mind, we consulted, and agreed to send two of the men with a candle up the bank, in order to examine if it had separated from the island, a circumstance that we suspected, from hearing the snapping of the limbs of some drift trees, which were deposited betwixt the margin of the river, and the summit of the bank. The men, on arriving at the edge of the river, cried out " *Venez à terre! Venez à terre!* and told us there was a chasm formed already, so wide that it would be difficult to pass it, to attain the firm ground. I ordered them to go upon the island and make a fire, and desired Mr. Bridge and the *patron* to follow them; and as it now occurred to me that the preservation of the boat in a great measure depended on the depth of the river, I tried with a sounding pole, and to my great joy, found it did not exceed eight or ten feet.

Immediately after the shock we noticed the time, and found it was near two o'clock. It was now nearly half past, and I determined to go ashore myself, after securing some papers and money, and was employed in taking them out of my trunks, when another shock came on, terrible indeed, but not equal to the first. Morin, our *patron*, called out from the island, " *Monsieur Bradbury ! sauvez vous, sauvez vous !*" I went ashore, and found the chasm really frightful, as it was not less than four feet in width, and besides the bank had sunk at least two feet. I took the candle, and examined to determine its length, and concluded that it could not be less than eighty yards; and where it terminated at each end, the banks had fallen into the river. I now saw clearly that our lives had been saved by having moored to a sloping bank. Before we had completed our fire, we had two more shocks, and they occurred during the whole night, at intervals of from six to ten minutes, but slight in comparison with the first and second. At four o'clock I took a candle, and again examined the bank, and found to my great satisfaction that no material alteration had taken place; I also found the boat safe, and secured my pocket compass, I had already noticed that the sound which was heard at the time of every shock, always preceded it at least a second, and that it always proceeded from the same point, and went off in an opposite direction. I now found that the shock came from a little northward of east, and proceeded to the westward. At day-light we had counted twenty-seven shocks, during our stay on the island, but still found the chasm so that it might be passed. The river was covered with foam and drift timber, and had risen considerably, but our boat was safe. Whilst we were waiting till the light became sufficient for us to embark, two canoes floated down the river, in one of which we could perceive some Indian corn and some clothes. We considered this as a melancholy proof that some of the boats we passed the preceding day had perished. Our conjectures were afterwards confirmed, as three had been overwhelmed, and all on board perished. When the daylight appeared to be sufficient for us, I gave orders to embark, and we all went on board. Two men were in the act of loosening the fastenings, when a shock occurred nearly equal to the first in violence. The men ran up the bank, in order to save themselves on the island, but before they could get over the chasm, a tree fell close by them, and stopped their progress. The bank appeared to me to be moving rapidly into the river, and I called out to the men in the boat " *Coupex*

les cordes !" on hearing this, the two men ran down
the bank, loosed the cords, and jumped into the boat.
We now found ourselves again on the river : the
Chenal du Diable was in sight, and appeared absolutely impassable, from the quantity of trees and
drift wood, that had lodged during the night
against the planters fixed in the bottom of the river; and in addition to our difficulties, I noticed
that the *patron* and the men appeared to be so terrified and confused, as to be almost incapable of
action. I determined to stop, previous to passing
the channel, in order that the men might have
time to become more composed. I had the good
fortune to discover a bank, rising with a gentle
slope, where we again moored, and prepared to
breakfast on the island. Whilst that was preparing, I walked down the island, in company with
Morin, our *patron*, to view the channel, in order
to ascertain the safest part, which we soon agreed
upon. Whilst we were thus employed, we experienced a very severe shock, and found some difficulty in preserving ourselves from being thrown
down; another occurred during the time we were
at breakfast, and a third as we were preparing to
reimbark. In the last, Mr. Bridge, who was standing within the declivity of the bank, narrowly escaped being thrown into the river, as the sand continued to give way under his feet. As I observed
that the men were still very much under the influ-

ence of terror, I desired Morin to give to each a glass of spirits, and reminded them that their safety depended on their exertions, and we pushed out into the river. The danger we had now to encounter was of a nature which they understood: the nearer we approached it, the more confidence they appeared to gain; and indeed, all their strength, and all the skill of Morin, was necessary, as there was no direct channel through the trees, and we were several times under the necessity of changing our course in the space of a few seconds, and that instantaneously, not a moment being left for deliberation. Immediately after we had cleared all danger, the men dropped their oars, crossed themselves, and gave a shout, congratulating each other on our safety.

We continued on the river till eleven o'clock, when there was a violent shock, which seemed to affect us as sensibly as if we had been on land. The trees on both sides of the river were most violently agitated, and the banks fell in, in several places, within our view, carrying with them innumerable trees, the crash of which falling into the river, mixed with the terrible sound attending the shock, and the screaming of the geese, and other wild-fowl, produced an idea that all nature was in a state of dissolution. During the shock, the river had been much agitated, and the men became anxious to go ashore : my opinion was, that we were much more safe on the river; but finding that they laid down their oars, and seemed determined to quit the boat for the present, we looked out for a part of the river where we might moor it in security, and having found one, we stopped during the remainder of the day.

At three o'clock, another canoe passed us adrift on the river. We did not experience any more shocks until the morning of the 17th, when two occurred; one about five, and the other about seven o'clock. We continued our voyage, and about twelve this day, had a severe shock, of very long duration. About four o'clock came in sight of a log-house, a little above the Lower Chickasaw Bluffs. More than twenty people came out as soon as they discovered us, and when within hearing, earnestly entreated us to come ashore. I found them almost distracted with fear, and that they were composed of several families, who had collected in order that they might pray together. On entering the house, I saw a bible lying open on the table. They informed me that the greatest part of the inhabitants in the neighbourhood had fled to the hills, on the opposite side of the river, for safety; and that during the shock, about sun-rise on the 16th, a chasm had opened on the sand bar opposite the bluffs below, and on closing again, had thrown the water to the height of a tall tree. They also affirmed that the earth opened in several places back from the river. One of the men, who appeared to be considered as possessing more knowledge than the rest, entered into an explanation of of the cause, and attributed it to the comet that had appeared a few months before, which he described as having two horns, over one of which the earth had rolled, and was now lodged betwixt them : that the shocks were occasioned by the attempts made by the earth to surmount the other horn. If this should be accomplished, all would be well, if otherwise, inevitable destruction to the world would follow. Finding him confident in his hypothesis, and myself unable to refute it, I did not dispute the point, and we went on about a mile further. Only one shock occurred this night, at half past seven o'clock. On the morning of the 18th, two shocks, one betwixt three and four o'clock, and the other at six. At noon, a violent one, of very long duration, which threw a great number of trees into the river within our view. In the evening, two slight shocks, one at six, the other at nine o'clock.

19th.—We arrived at the mouth of the river St. Francis, and had only one shock, which happened at eleven at night.

20th.—Detained by fog, and experienced only two shocks, one at five, the other at seven in the evening.

21st.—Awakened by a shock at half past four o'clock : this was the last, and not very violent, but lasted for nearly a minute.

On the 24th in the evening, we saw a smoke, and knowing that there were no habitations on this part of the river, we made towards it, and found it to be the camp of a few Choctaw Indians, from whom I purchased a swan, for five balls and five loads of powder.

25th.—Monsieur Longpre overtook us, and we encamped together in the evening. He was about 200 miles from us on the night of the 15th, by the course of the river, where the earthquakes had also been very terrible. It appeared from his account, that at New Madrid the shock had been extreme-ly violent: the greatest part of the houses had been rendered uninhabitable, although, being construct-ed of timber, and framed together, they were better calculated to withstand the shocks than buildings of brick or stone. The greatest part of the plain on which the town was situated was become a lake, and the houses deserted.

The remainder of our voyage to Natches was very pleasant, except two very narrow escapes from *planters* in the river; and without any occurrence that would excite much interest, we arrived at the port of Natchez on the afternoon of the 5th of January, and went to the city, which is situated about three quarters of a mile from the river, on the level behind the bluffs. The port consists of thirty or forty houses, and some stores : for the size of it, there is not, perhaps, in the world a more dissipated place. Almost all the Kentucky men stop here on the way to Orleans, and as they now consider all the dangers and difficulties of their voyage as past, they feel the same inclination to dissipation as sailors who have been long out of port, and generally remain here a day or two to indulge it. I spent a very agreeable evening in the city, in company with Dr. Brown, whom I found to be an exceedingly pleasant and intelligent man.

In the morning of the 6th instant I went on board the steam boat from Pittsburgh; she had passed us at the mouth of the Arkansas, 341 miles above Natchez; she was a very handsome vessel, of 410 tons burden, and was impelled by a very powerful steam engine, also made at Pittsburg, from whence she had come in less than twenty days, although 1900 miles distance. About eighty miles above New Orleans, the sugar plantations commenced, some of which I visited, accompanied by Mr. Longpre, who assured me that he had not seen the cane in higher perfection in any part of the West Indies. Many fields yet remained, from which the cane had not been got in, and were now covered with snow, an occurrence, as I was informed, very uncommon. From this part to New Orleans, groves of orange trees of great extent are seen on both sides of the river, and at this season, loaded with ripe fruit.

On the 13th we arrived at New Orleans, where I consigned the lead to the agent of Mr. Drinker, again met with my friend Brackenridge, and on the 20th set sail for New York.

APPENDIX.

APPENDIX.

No. I.

VOCABULARY OF SOME WORDS

IN THE

OSAGE LANGUAGE.

Man,	*Ne-ka.*
Woman,	*Wa-ko.*
Boy,	*Shin-zo shin-ga.*
Girl,	*She-ma shin-ga.*
Young man,	*Shen-don-sho.*
Young woman,	*Kas-ho-mĕ.*
Old man,	*Ke-sau-ga hin-ga.*
Old woman,	*Wa-ko hin-ga.*
Head,	*Wa-augh-reh.*
Nose,	*Pa-gĕ.*
Mouth,	*E-haugh.*
Chin,	*La-baugh.*
Face,	*In-ga.*
Throat,	*To-ja.*
Arm,	*Haugh.*

Hand,	*Nom-ba.*
Breast,	*Mo-in-ga.*
Belly,	*Che-sa.*
Thigh,	*Sha-gaugh omba.*
Knee,	*Se-don-ja.*
Leg,	*Sha-gaugh.*
Calf of Leg.	*E-sho.*
Shin,	*Wa-haugh.*
Ancle,	*He-ka.*
Foot,	*See.*
Toe,	*See-paugh.*
Finger,	*Sha-ga.*
Finger nails,	*Sha-ga hugh.*
Horse,	*Kou-olă.*
Mare,	*Kou-o-lă mingă.*
Colt,	*Kou-o-lă shin-ga.*
Bull,	*Shes-ka ton-ga.*
Cow,	*Shes-ka min-gă.*
Buffaloe bull,	*Sha tonga.*
Ditto cow,	*Sha.*
Elk, male,	*O-pa ton-ga.*
Do. female,	*O-pa mingă.*
Deer, male,	*Taw ton-ga.*
Do. female,	*Taw min-gă.*
Fawn,	*Sha-ra-sha shin-ga.*
Bear, male,	*Was-saw-ba ton-ga.*
Do. female,	*Was-saw-ba min-gă.*
Wolf,	*Sho-ma ca-sa.*
Dog,	*Shon-ga.*

Fox,	*Mou-shu lo-go-nĕ.*
Cat,	*E-gron-ga-sha.*
Beaver,	*Sha-ba.*
Otter,	*Tow-non-ja.*
Squirrel,	*Se-in-ja.*
Rabbit,	*Mos-tin-ja.*
Panther,	*E-gron-ga.*
Skunk,	*Mon-ga.*
Rattlesnake,	*Sha-kee.*
Black snake,	*Wait-saw sau-ba.*
Frog,	*Pa-nis-ka.*
Spider,	*Shaw-bas-ka.*
Turkey cock,	*Su-ka ton-ga.*
Ditto hen,	*Suka.*
Goose,	*Me-has-shaw-ba.*
Swan,	*Me-has-ca.*
Dunghill cock,	*Su-ka shu-ga ton-ga.*
Hen,	*Su-ka shu-ga.*
Crow,	*Ka-wa.*
Raven,	*Ka-wa ton-ga.*
Hawk,	*Was-sa shin-ga ton-ga.*
Eagle,	*Hu-ras-po-sa.*
Vulture,	*Ha-ja.*
Owl,	*Waw-po-jă.*
Fish,	*Hoe.*
An American,	*Moi-hĕ ton-ga.*
An Englishman,	*Me-gra-sha.*
A Frenchman,	*Es-ta-wĕ.*
A Spaniard,	*Esh-pa-nuo.*

Sugar,	*Shau-na.*
Salt,	*Ne-shu.*
Tobacco,	*No-ne-agh.*
Pipe,	*No-nem-ba.*
Gun,	*Wau-ho-ton.*
Cannon.	*Wau-ho-ton ton-ga.*
Pistol,	*Wau-ho-ton-da paugh.*
Gunpowder.	*Ne-hu-ja wa-ca-ja.*
Lead,	*Mos-sa ma-jos-ca.*
Flint,	*Moi-hu-sĕ.*
Powder-horn,	*Sha-ka.*
Knife,	*Moi-hĕ.*
Tomahawk,	*Moi-hĕ sa-pạ shinga.*
Axe,	*Moi-hĕ shaw-a-ga-sa.*
Hoe,	*Mon-sa-vă.*
Kettle,	*Sha-ha.*
Tin cup,	*Kes-ne-la-tă.*
Saddle,	*Hon-ko-gra.*
Hair,	*Pa-us-ka.*
Beads,	*Hes-ka.*
Wampum,	*Hes-ka wa-num-pĕ.*
Vermillion,	*Wa-su-ga.*
Medal,	*Ca-ha-ga.*
Cloth,	*Ḥau.*
Red cloth,	*Hau shu-ja.*
White cloth,	*Hau ska.*
Black cloth, &c. &c.	*Hau sau-ba.*
One,	*Mi-ne-hĕ.*
Two,	*Nom-baugh.*

Three,	*Lau-be-na.*
Four,	*To-ba.*
Five,	*Sat-ta.*
Six,	*Sha-pa.*
Seven,	*Pa-nom-ba.*
Eight,	*Ke-lan-baugh.*
Nine,	*Shan-ka.*
Ten	*Cra-bra.*
Eleven,	*Au-grĕ mi ne-hĕ.*
Twelve,	*Au-grĕ nom-baugh.*
Thirteen &c. to twenty,	*Augrĕ lau-be-na.*
One hundred,	*Cra-bra ton-ga.*
River,	*Nes-ka.*
Prairie,	*Ton-ja.*
Woodland,	*Son-ja.*
A garrison,	*Nau-sa.*
Village,	*To-wa-nĕ.*
A commanding officer,	*Kaw-he-ja wau-ton-ga.*
Physician,	*Wa-ken-da-ga.*
Father,	*In-da-ja.*
Mother,	*E-naugh..*
Brother,	*Wee-shin-da.*
Sister,	*Wee-ton-ja.*
Uncle,	*Ween-ja-kĕ.*
Aunt,	*Wee-she-mee.*
Brother-in-law,	*Wee-ton-ha.*
Water,	*Nes-nigh.*
Ice,	*Non-ha.*
Snow,	*Pau.*

P

Rain,	*Nigh-shu.*
Frost,	*Pau-shu.*
Winter,	*Bor-ra.*
Summer,	*To-ja-ton.*
Spring,	*Pa-ton.*
Autumn,	*Ton-da.*
Hot,	*Most-cha.*
Cold,	*Ne-wat-cha.*
Red,	*Shu-ja.*
White,	*Ska,*
Black,	*Sau-ba.*
Blue,	*To-ha.*
Yellow,	*Se-a.*
Green,	*Ne-a-ko.*
House,	*Tee-he.*
Door,	*Tee-he sha-ba.*
Robe,	*Mes-co-ba.*
Blanket,	*Aug-re.*
Mockasons	*Hom-ba.*
Leggings,	*He-minca.*
Soldier,	*Has-ha-ke-da.*
Large,	*Gron-da.*
Largest,	*Ton-ga.*
Small,	*Wau-ho-ka.*
Smaller,	*Shin-ga.*
Ugly,	*Pe-sha.*
Handsome,	*Lo-go-ne.*
Yes,	*Hoy-a.*
No,	*Hon-kos-ka.*

Good,	*Lo-go-ne,* or *Tou-ha.*
Bad,	*Pe-sha.*
President of the United States,	*Kow-a-ga Show-a-ga Wa-ge-shu.*
Large man,	*Ne-ka she-ga gronda.*
Large body of men,	*Ne-ka she-ga hugh.*
Flock of deer,	*Tau-hugh.*
Large flock of birds,	*Was-sa shin-ga hugh.*
Drove of buffaloes,	*Sha-to-ga ochĕ.*
Scalp,	*Ne-shu-ha-du-sa.*
Run,	*Tau-nĕ.*
Come,	*Ku-e-lo.*
To go,	*Mo-gre-na.*
Kill,	*Es-sa-ra.*
Leap,	*We-she.*
Me,	*We-ah.*
You,	*De-ah.*
Day,	*Hon-pa.*
Night,	*He-nĕ.*
Light,	*Hon-pa lo-go-nĕ.*
Dark,	*He-nĕ pe-sha.*
To part asunder,	*We-ta.*
To join,	*Sho-sho.*
To eat,	*Wa-num-bra.*
To drink,	*Ne-bra-ta.*
To sleep,	*A-shem-bra.*
To get up,	*Pau-haw.*
To walk,	*O-ga-sha.*
To lie down,	*Au-re-con-sha.*

No. II.

ORATION DELIVERED BY THE BIG ELK,

THE CHIEF OF THE MAHA NATION,

OVER THE GRAVE OF THE BLACK BUFFALOE,

CHIEF OF THE TETONS, A TRIBE OF THE SIOUX,

AT THE PORTAGE DES SIOUX,

14th July, 1813.

Do not grieve—misfortunes will happen to the wisest and best men. Death will come, and always comes out of season :—it is the command of the Great Spirit, and all nations and people must obey. What is passed, and cannot be prevented, should not be grieved for. Be not discouraged or displeased then, that in visiting your father here, you have lost your chief. A misfortune of this kind may never again befal you, but this would have attended you perhaps at your own village. Five times have I visited this land, and never returned with sorrow or pain. Misfortunes do not flourish particularly in our path—they grow every where. *(Addressing himself to Governor Edwards and Colonel Miller.)* What a misfortune for me that I could not have died this day, instead of the

chief that lies before us. The trifling loss my nation would have sustained in my death, would have
been doubly paid for by the honours of my burial—
they would have wiped off every thing like regret.
Instead of being covered with a cloud of sorrow—
my warriors would have felt the sunshine of joy in
their hearts. To me it would have been a most
glorious occurrence. Hereafter, when I die at
home, instead of a noble grave and a grand procession, the rolling music and the thundering cannon,
with a flag waving at my head, I shall be wrapped
in a robe, (an old robe perhaps) and hoisted on a
slender scaffold to the whistling winds, soon to be
blown down to the earth—my flesh to be devoured
by the wolves, and my bones rattled on the plain
by the wild beasts. *(Addressing himself to Colonel
Miller.)* Chief of the soldiers—your labours have
not been in vain:—your attention shall not be for-
gotten. My nation shall know the respect that is
paid over the dead. When I return I will echo
the sound of your guns.

No. III.

THE FOLLOWING INTERESTING NARRATIVE

OF THE

EXPEDITION OF MR. HUNT,

MENTIONED IN THIS WORK, IS EXTRACTED FROM THE MISSOURI GAZETTE.

WE last week promised our readers an account of the journey of the gentlemen attached to the New York Fur Company, from the Pacific Ocean to this place.—We now lay it before our readers, as collected from the gentlemen themselves.

On the 28th of June, 1812, Mr. Robert Stewart, one of the partners of the Pacific Fur Company, with two Frenchmen, Mr. Ramsey Crooks, and Mr. Robert M'Clellan, left the Pacific Ocean with despatches for New York.

After ascending the Columbia river ninety miles, John Day, one of the hunters, became perfectly insane, and was sent back to the main establishment, under the charge of some Indians: the remaining six pursued their voyage upwards of six hundred miles, when they happily met with Mr. Joseph Miller, on his way to the mouth of the Columbia. He had been considerably to the south and east, among the nations called *Blackarms* and *Arapahays*, by the latter of whom he was robbed; in consequence of which he suffered almost every privation human nature is capable of, and was in a state of starvation and almost nudity when the party met him.

They had now fifteen horses, and pursued their journey for the Atlantic world, without any uncommon accident, until within about two hundred miles of the Rocky Mountains, where they unfortunately met with a party of the Crow Indians, who behaved with the most unbounded insolence, and were solely prevented from cutting off the party by observing them well armed and constantly on their guard. They, however, pursued on their track six days, and finally stole every horse belonging to the party.

Some idea of the situation of those men may be conceived, when we take into consideration, that they were now on foot, and had a journey of two thousand miles before them, fifteen hundred of which was entirely unknown, as they intended and prosecuted it considerably south of Messrs. Lewis and Clarke's route. The impossibility of carrying any quantity of provisions on their backs, in addition to their ammunition and bedding, will occur at first view. The danger to be apprehended from starvation was imminent. They, however, put the best face upon their prospects, and pursued their route towards the Rocky Mountains, at the head waters of the Colorado, or Spanish River, and stood their course E. S. E. until they struck the head waters of the great River Platte, which they undeviatingly followed to its mouth. It may here be observed, that this river, for about two hundred miles, is navigable for a barge; from thence to the Otto Village, within 45 miles of its entrance into the Missouri, it is a mere bed of sand, without water sufficient to float a skin canoe.

From the Otto Village to St. Louis, the party performed their voyage in a canoe, furnished them by the natives, and arrived here in perfect health, on the 30th of last month (May.)

Our travellers did not hear of the war with England until they came to the Ottos. These people told them, that the Shawnoe Prophet had sent them a wampum, inviting them to join in the war against the Americans. They answered the messenger, that they could make more by trapping beaver than making war against the Americans.

After crossing the hills (Rocky Mountains) they fell in with a small party of Snake Indians, from whom they purchased a horse, which relieved them from any further carriage of food, and this faithful four-footed companion, performed that service to the Otto Village. They wintered on the river Platte, six hundred miles from its mouth.

By information received from these gentlemen, it appears that a journey across the continent of North America might be performed with a waggon, there being no obstruction in the whole route that any person would dare to call a mountain, in addition to its being much the most direct and short one to go from this place to the mouth of the Columbia river. Any future party, who may undertake this journey, and are tolerably acquainted with the different places where it would be necessary to lay up a small stock of provisions, would not be impeded, as, in all probability, they would not meet with an Indian to interrupt their progress, although on the other route, more north, there are almost insurmountable barriers.

The following is Mr. Crooks's narrative of Mr. Hunt's expedition from the Aricaras to the Pacific:

Messrs. Hunt, Crooks, Miller, M'Clellan, M'Kenzie, and about sixty men, who left St. Louis in the beginning of March, 1811, for the Pacific

Ocean, reached the Aricara village on the 13th day
of June, where meeting with some American
hunters, who had been the preceding year on the
waters of the Columbia with Mr. Henry, and who,
giving such an account of the route by which they
passed, as being far preferable in point of procuring with facility an abundant supply of food at all
times, as well as avoiding even the probability of
seeing their enemies, the Black Feet, than by the
track of Captains Lewis and Clarke, the gentlemen of the expedition at once abandoned their
former ideas of passing by the Falls of the Missouri, and made the necessary arrangements for
commencing their journey over land from this
place.

Eighty horses were purchased and equipped by
the 17th of July, and on the day following they de-
parted from the Aricaras, sixty persons in number,
all on foot, except the partners of the company.—
In this situation they proceeded for five days, having crossed, in that time, two considerable streams,
which joined the Missouri below the Aricaras,
when, finding an inland tribe of Indians, calling
themselves Shawhays, but known among the whites
by the appellation of Chiennes, they procured from
these an accession of forty horses, which enabled
the gentlemen to furnish a horse for every two
men. Steering about W. S. W. they passed the
small branches of Big River, the Little Missouri,

above its forks, and several of the tributary streams of Powder River, one of which they followed up. They found a band of the Absaroka, or Crow nation, encamped on its banks, at the foot of the Big Horn Mountain.

For ammunition and some small articles, they exchanged all their lame for sound horses, with these savages; but although that this band has been allowed by every one who knew them, to be, by far, the best behaved of their tribe, it was only by that unalterable determination of the gentlemen to avoid jeopardizing the safety of the party, without, at the same moment, submitting to intentional insults, that they left this camp (not possessing a greater force than the whites) without coming to blows.

The distance from the Aricaras to this mountain, is about 450 miles, over an extremely rugged tract, by no means furnishing a sufficient supply of water: but during the twenty-eight days they were getting to the base of the mountain, they were only in a few instances without abundance of buffaloe meat.

Three days took them over the plains of Mad River, (the name given to the Big Horn above this mountain) which following for a number of days, they left it where it was reduced to eighty yards in width, and the same evening reached the banks of the Colorada, or Spanish River. Finding flocks of buffaloe at the end of the third day's travel on this stream, the party passed a week in drying buffaloe meat, for the residue of the voyage, as in all probability those were the last animals of the kind they would meet with. From this camp, in one day, they crossed the Dividing Mountain, and pitched their tents on Hoback's Fork of Mad River, where it was near 150 feet broad; and in eight days more, having passed several stupendous ridges, they encamped in the vicinity of the establishment made by Mr. Henry, in the fall of 1810, on a fork about seventy yards wide, bearing the name of that gentleman: having travelled from the main Missouri, about 900 miles, in fifty-four days. Here, abandoning their horses, the party constructed canoes, and descended the Snake, or Ky-eye-nem River, (made by the junction of Mad River, south of Henry's Fork) 400 miles; in the course of which they were obliged, by the intervention of impassable rapids, to make a number of portages; till at length they found the river confined between gloomy precipices, at least 200 feet perpendicular, whose banks for the most part were washed by this turbulent stream, which for thirty miles was a continual succession of falls, cascades, and rapids. Mr. Crooks' canoe had split and upset in the middle of a rapid, by which one man was

drowned, named Antonie Clappin, and Mr. Crooks
saved himself only by extreme exertion in swim-
ing. From the repeated losses by the upsetting
of canoes, their provisions were now reduced to a
bare sufficiency for five days, totally ignorant of
the country where they were, and unsuccessful in
meeting any of the nations from whom they could
hope for information.

Unable to proceed by water, Messrs. M'Kenzie,
M'Clellan, and Reed set out in different directions
down the river, for the purpose of finding Indians,
and buying horses. Mr. Crooks, with a few men,
returned to Henry's Fork for those they had left,
while Mr. Hunt remained with the main body of
men, entrapping beaver for their support. Mr.
Crooks, finding the distance much greater by land
than he had contemplated, returned at the end of
three days; where waiting five more, expecting
relief from below, the near approach of winter
made them determine on depositing all superfluous
articles, and proceeding on foot. Accordingly, on
the 10th of November, Messrs. Hunt and Crooks
set out, each with eighteen men; one party on the
south side of the river. Mr. Hunt was fortunate
in finding Indians, with abundance of salmon, and
some horses; but Mr. Crooks saw but few, and
in general too miserably poor to afford his party
assistance. Thirteen days brought the latter to a

high range of mountains, through which the river forced a passage, and the banks being their only guide, they still, by climbing over points of rocky ridges projecting into the stream, kept as near to it as possible, till in the evening of the 3d of December, impassable precipices, of immense height, put an end to all hopes of following the margin of this water course, which here was no more than forty yards wide, ran with incredible velocity, and was withal so foamingly tumultuous, that even had the opposite bank been fit for their purpose, attempts at rafting would have been perfect madness, as they could only have the inducement of ending, in a watery grave, a series of hardships and privations, to which the most hardy and determined of the human race must have found himself inadequate. They attempted to climb the mountains, still bent on pushing on, but after ascending for half a day, they discovered to their sorrow, that they were not half way to the summit, and the snow already too deep for men in their emaciated state to proceed further.

Regaining the river bank, they returned up, and on the third day met with Mr. Hunt and party, with one horse, proceeding downwards. A canoe was soon made of a horse hide, and in it they transported some meat, which they could spare, to Mr. Crooks' starving followers, who, for the first eighteen

days, after leaving the place of deposit, had subsisted on half a meal in twenty-four hours, and in
the last nine days had eaten only one beaver, a dog,
a few wild cherries, and some old mockason soles,
having travelled, during these twenty-seven days,
at least five hundred and fifty miles. For the next
four days, both parties continued their course up
the river, without any other support than what little
rose-buds and cherries they could find; but here
they luckily fell in with some Snake Indians, from
whom they got five horses, giving them three guns
and some other articles for the same.

Starvation had bereft J. B. Provost of his senses
entirely, and on seeing the horse flesh on the opposite side of the river, he was so agitated in crossing in
a skin canoe, that he upset it, and was unfortunately
drowned. From hence Mr. Hunt went on to a
camp of Shoshonies, about ninety miles above, where
procuring a few horses and a guide, he set out for
the main Columbia, across the mountains of the
south west, leaving the river where it entered the
range, and on it Mr. Crooks and five men, unable
to travel, Mr. Hunt lost a Canadian, named Carrier,
by starvation, before he met the Shy-eye-to-ga Indians in the Columbia plains; from whom, getting
a supply of provisions, he soon reached the main
river, which he descended in canoes, and arrived

without any further loss at Astoria in the month of February.

Messrs. M‘Kenzie, M‘Clelland, and Reed, had united their parties on the Snake River Mountains, through which they travelled twenty-one days, to the Mulpot River, subsisting on an allowance by no means adequate to the toils they underwent daily; and to the smallness of their number (which was in all eleven) they attribute their success in getting with life to where they found some wild horses. They soon after reached the Forks, called by Captains Lewis and Clarke, Koolkooske; went down Lewis's River and the Columbia wholly by water, without any misfortune except the upsetting, in a rapid, of Mr. M‘Clelland's canoe; and although it happened on the first day of the year, yet, by great exertion, they clang to the canoe till the others came to their assistance, making their escape with the loss of some rifles. They reached Astoria early in January.

Three of the five men who remained with Mr. Crooks, afraid of perishing by want, left him in February, on a small river on the road, by which Mr. Hunt had passed, in quest of Indians, and have not since been heard of. Mr. Crooks had followed Mr. Hunt's track in the snow for seven days; but coming to a low prairie, he lost every appearance of a trace, and was compelled to pass the remaining part of winter in mountains, subsisting sometimes on beaver and horse meat, and their skins, and at others on their success in finding roots. Finally, on the last of March, the other only Canadian being unable to proceed, was left with a lodge of Shoshonies, and Mr. Crooks, with John Day, finding the snow sufficiently diminished, undertook, from Indian information, to cross the last ridge, which they happily effected, and reached the banks of the Columbia in the middle of April; where, in the beginning of May, they fell in with Messrs. Stewart and Co. having been, a few days before, stripped of every thing they possessed by a band of villains near the Falls. On the 10th of May they arrived safe at Astoria, the principal establishment of the Pacific Fur Company, within fourteen miles of Cape Disappointment.*

---

* This establishment has since been broken up.

DESCRIPTION

OF THE

MISSOURI TERRITORY.

THE Missouri Territory is bounded by the state of
Louisiana on the south, the Mississippi on the east,
the British Territory on the north, and by the Rocky
Mountains and Mexico on the west. It was first
discovered by Sebastian Cabot, in the year 1497,
and in the year 1512 it was visited by John Pontio
de Leon, a Spaniard, who attempted to form a settlement. In 1684, Monsieur de la Salle, a Frenchman, discovered the mouth of the Mississippi, and
built Fort Louis; but being assassinated, it was
again abandoned. In the year 1698, Captain Ib-
berville sailed up the Mississippi, formed a settlement, and named the country Louisiana. About
twenty-two years afterwards Monsieur de la Sueur
also sailed up the Mississippi, and proceeded to the
distance of 2280 miles from its mouth.

In 1762 France ceded it to Spain by a secret treaty, and a small force was sent to take possession; but the inhabitants not having been officially made acquainted with the cession, refused to submit to the dominion of that power. Some time afterwards the Spanish government commissioned a man named O'Reilly, at the head of 3000 men, who took possession of it, and from motives of revenge, put several of the principal inhabitants to death. In 1800, 1801, Spain ceded it back to France, and by a treaty of April 30th, 1803, the French government sold it to the United States for the sum of fifteen millions of dollars, payable in fifteen years, at one million annually. The extent of country purchased for this sum is not yet known with any considerable degree of accuracy, but is calculated to contain at least 1,026,312 square miles, or 656,839,680 acres, and it must be remembered that for this sum not only the political dominion, but the reversionary property in the land, was purchased. If we suppose the money to apply to the purchase of the land only, the cost will fall short of 1¼d. per acre, or £3, 6s. 8d. sterling per square mile, without one drop of blood being shed.*

---

* By the most accurate calculation, the surface of the globe contains 198,976,786 square miles, one-fifth of which only is land, or 39,795,357 square miles, the value of which is

The Mississippi receives the water furnished by almost the whole of this area, and as the extent of country from which it derives its water is pretty accurately known, I shall state it, that an adequate idea may be formed of that mighty river; but I will previously observe that the name is of Indian origin, and signifies " *The mother of the waters.*"

From the extremity of the most eastern branch to that of the most western, it is 1680 miles in a direct line; and from the commencement of the most northerly to its mouth, is 1650, also in a direct line.

Amongst the immense advantages which the United States will derive from the purchase of Louisiana, the possession of this river is one of the greatest. The whole territory of the United States is 1,205,635,840 acres. The following table will show that the area dependent on the Mississippi for a communication with the ocean, is 1,344,779 square miles, or 860,658,560 acres. The whole empire of China is only estimated at 800,000,000 of acres!

£132,651,190 sterling, at £3, 6s. 8d. per square mile; from whence it appears that at this price the cost of seven worlds, as large as this we inhabit, would be only £928,558,330!!! Should any one doubt the wisdom of Mr. Jefferson, after being acquainted with this fact, let him enter into a calculation of the expences incurred in the *old mode* of acquiring territory by the sword. He will soon convince himself that this is a very much improved plan.

The area of the states or territories, or of the portions of such as contribute to the waters of this river are as follow :—

		Sqr. Miles.
Missouri Territory,	....	985,250
North-West Territory, $\frac{1}{3}$,	....	53,415
Illinois Territory (the whole),	....	52,000
Indiana State, $\frac{19}{20}$,	....	37,050
Ohio State, $\frac{4}{5}$,	....	35,088
Pennsylvania, $\frac{1}{3}$,	....	16,493
New York, $\frac{1}{100}$,	....	521
Maryland, $\frac{1}{100}$,	....	140
Virginia, $\frac{2}{5}$,	....	28,200
Kentucky (the whole),	....	40,110
Tennessee (ditto),	....	43,200
Mississippi Territory, $\frac{1}{3}$,	....	29,560
State of Orleans, $\frac{1}{2}$,	....	20,500
Georgia, $\frac{1}{30}$,	....	2,000
North Carolina, $\frac{1}{50}$,	....	1,100
South Carolina, $\frac{1}{150}$,	....	152

Square miles, ... 1,344,779

This area is nearly twenty-eight times the extent of England and Wales, and eleven times that of the whole of Great Britain and Ireland.

Mr. Mellish enters into a calculation of the quantity of water discharged by this river at its mean height ; but notwithstanding his usual accuracy, I think he has erred in this case, by taking a wrong data. In the first place, he has made his estimate of the magnitude of the river by considering it at its mouth, without taking into account the great number of *bayoux* that have previously issued from it. Even at Orleans its magnitude is much diminished. Amongst other *bayoux* that take water from this river above that city, are *bayou Chiffalie, bayou Tunica, bayou Manchac, La Fourche,* and *Placqmines.* In other places any of these five *bayoux* would be considered as a great river; but here a comparison with their vast parent destroys their consequence. It is singular that the Mississippi maintains its full magnitude only for the length of three miles. At that distance from the mouth of Red River issues bayou Chiffalie.

The second error consists in not allowing sufficient depth to the river. He assumes forty feet as the average depth from Orleans to the mouth, whereas it is well known that at that city the depth is sixty fathoms, or 360 feet, and in no part from thence to the bar at its mouth is it less than thirteen fathoms, or 78 feet. But although he has assumed the dimensions of the river at too little, he has erred greatly in the calculation founded thereon, by making the discharge of water five times more than his own data will produce. He considers the river at two miles in breadth, forty feet in depth, and to run four miles per hour. This gives, he says,

94,000,000 of gallons per second, whereas it is only 18,537,325 gallons. Perhaps about 60,000,000 of gallons per second, at a mean state betwixt Red River and bayou Chiffalie, may not be far from the true quantity.

The territory west of the Mississippi belonging to the United States, and extending from that river to the rocky mountains has evidently two characters, so distinct, as regards the external appearance, that they cannot justly be inclosed in one general description. The part which lies immediately on the Mississippi, and extends from 100 to 250 miles westward from that river, has a thin covering of timber, consisting of clumps and of scattered trees. From the western limits of this region to the Rocky Mountains, the whole is one vast prairie or meadow, and, excepting on the alluvion of the rivers, and, in a few instances, on the sides of the small hills, is entirely divested of trees or shrubs. The extent of this region is not accurately known, on account of the real situation of the Rocky Mountains not yet being truly ascertained; but it appears from the account of hunters and travellers, that in some of our best maps and globes they are laid down considerably too far to the eastward. The course of the Mississippi is nearly from north to south, and its average longitude nearly 90 degrees west. The coast of the Pacific, in the medium latitude of the

Mississippi from its source to its mouth, is about 130 degrees west, a difference of 40 degrees, making in that latitude the distance from the Mississippi to the Pacific to be 2124 miles. It is the opinion of all whom I have consulted, and who have crossed the Rocky Mountains to the Pacific, that from the eastern limits of that chain to the Mississippi, the distance is at least twice as great as from the western limit to the Pacific.* If this is admitted to be correct, the distance from the summit of the Rocky Mountains to the Mississippi is 1416 miles, from which if 150 be subtracted for the half breadth of the chain, and 200 for the woody region on the Mississippi, the breadth of the prairie will appear to be 1066 miles, and its length, from north to south is at least 18 degrees of latitude, or 1251 miles.

Excepting towards the foot of the Rocky Mountains, the whole of this extent is what is usually termed a plain, being destitute of those elevations that in other parts appear to have resulted from convulsions. But although the *general* surface corresponds almost exactly with the convexity of the earth, the agency of water has produced innumerable shallow valleys; and of the elevated places

---

* Mr. Mellish asserts that one branch of the Missouri rises within 450 miles of the Pacific Ocean.

which separate them, those termed dividing ridges*
are the highest. From the top of any of these
ridges the limits of the visible horizon are as exactly defined, and the view as extensive as at sea,
the undulations on the surface of the earth here
bearing no greater proportion in the scale than the
waves of an agitated ocean. The deviation from
the true curvature of the earth is much greater on
the approach to the Rocky Mountains. This gives
an increased velocity to the currents of water, and
produces a more powerful attrition on their beds.
The consequence is, the valleys in that part are
deeper, and the surface more rugged and broken.

Several geological facts tend to prove that this
portion of the globe has been peculiarly exempted
from the operation of local and disorganizing convulsions, and that it has remained for a vast length
of time in its present state. The most prominent
of these facts is the undisturbed uniformity of the
strata, and their general parallelism to the surface
of the earth, as exemplified in the vast stratum of
iron ore on the Missouri, and in the limestone
rocks, wherever they occur. The depth and extent of the valleys of the river, together with the
peculiar formation of the hills, tend to confirm the
opinion, that whatever changes have taken place

---

* See note in page 60.

on the surface have been effected by the operations of a slow, but continually acting cause.

Some of the mineral deposits are of wonderful extent. Of these the deposit of salt on the Arkansas river is the most remarkable. So little of this is yet known, that an adequate idea of its magnitude can only be formed by taking into view the number of rivers constantly impregnated by it, and the extent of country from which they derive their sources. The most southerly of the salt rivers that rise in the region, containing this salt deposit, is a branch of Red River, called by the Indians *Ba-ha-cha-ha*, and by the French *Fouxoacheta*. It is a considerable stream, and salt rock is found on its banks. No fewer than three salt rivers or streams flow into the Arkansas, the least of which is fifty yards in breadth : another is seventy-five, and the largest is 150 yards wide. This last is called by the Osages *New-sew-kĕ tonga*, which signifies in their language, " *The largest salt river.*" These streams all rise in the same region, as also does a branch of the Canadian Fork of the Arkansas, another large river mentioned by Mr. Pike, the name of which he writes *Ne-sout-che-bra-ra*, which name indicates that either the water is salt, or that salt is found in the neighbourhood.*

---

* As the whole of this region is the property of the Osage Indians, it may justly be inferred that all the names of the rivers

It appears that this salt deposit passes under the Arkansas to the north west, and impregnates two branches of the Kanzas river of the Missouri, both of considerable magnitude. There are several salt deposits on this globe, of vast extent; but perhaps when this deposit becomes better ascertained, it will be found inferior to none in point of magnitude; for if its continuity in one body is a fact, the area it covers must amount to several thousand square miles.*

It is worthy of notice that gypsum and clay are found abounding with the salt of this deposit, and that in this instance, as well as in many others, the substances which are concomitant with each other

---

have originated with them. It is evident that Pike wrote the name from hearing the pronunciation, as the Indians do not write ; and had he attended to the derivation in this instance, he would have followed the same orthography as in the former, both being derived from *ne-shu,* or *new-sew* (salt), and *nes-ka,* or *nes-ke* (river). He would then have written it *New-sew-ke-bra-ra.*

* Mr. Sibly says the extent of this salt region is 75 miles square, which gives an area of 5625 square miles. Of the degree to which the water of these salt rivers is saturated, some idea may be formed when it is stated, that in the dry seasons the water of the Arkansas and Red Rivers are rendered very brackish by them. It appears also that it is the overflowing of one of these salt rivers that fills the Great Lake, which is evaporated every summer, and leaves the encrustation mentioned in page 186.

on this continent, correspond with the order observed in other parts of the world. Salt springs are very abundant in other parts west of the Mississippi. The body of iron ore on the Missouri is another instance of the magnitude of mineral deposits in this country. Some account of it may be seen in page 81.

From the accounts of hunters, the various indications of coal, and its frequent appearance, we may justly conclude that no portion of the earth is more abundant in that useful mineral than this region. It appears in various parts, at the foot of the bluffs of the Missouri. On the Osage River, a bed of very great, but unknown thickness, shews itself. On Red River it comes to the surface in several places, and the hunters speak of it as being one of the most common substances on the Little Missouri, and the Roche Jaune Rivers.

The existence of silver ore about the head of the Arkansas and Red River is believed by the inhabitants of Upper Louisiana, and various accounts are current amongst them of its having been discovered there by hunters. As those rivers rise in the range of mountains in which the mines of Santa Fe are situated, and not far distant from them, the account is probable; but the frequent occurrence of pyrites in America, the deceptive appearance of that substance, and the inability of men so little acquainted with mineralogy to discriminate, should induce great caution in admitting the fact.*

The part lying betwixt this vast meadow and the Mississippi river, it has already been stated, is of a different character as regards the external appearance of the country. This difference is not confined to the presence of trees in that part ; the surface of the country having also a different aspect. The numerous rivers falling into the Mississippi in this region, together with their various ramifications, run in deep and comparatively narrow valleys, which gives to this country a very uneven appearance. This is a necessary consequence

---

* In the interior of America, specimens of pyrites have been often shewn to me as the ore of silver or gold, and I have frequently found it an unpleasant task to undeceive those who were in possession of them, as they were persuaded that they had made a valuable discovery.

Immediately after I left the mouth of the Kenhawa river, I was followed to Galliopolis by a Quaker of the name of Kenzie, who shewed me some specimens of whitish pyrites, which he said was silver ore, and offered me a considerable sum of money if I would instruct him in the method of separating the metal. I attempted to undeceive him, but he became angry, and intimated that he knew the value of the mine too well to be *taken in that way*, and that it was no uncommon thing for Englishmen to discourage the working of mines in America, that they might get hold of them for themselves,

to the number of small rivers that fall *immediately* into the great trunk of the Mississippi. The general level of its bed, is at least 150 or 200 feet below that of the surrounding country. This gives a fall of that extent to the minor streams, besides that which is occasioned by the natural declivity of the country, and, of course, causes an increased velocity, and consequently a more powerful action on their beds : the effect extends to the smallest of the collateral branches. But although this portion differs so much from the other in its external appearance, still there are good reasons for thinking that they differ but little in their subterranean conformation, as many instances occur to prove, that although the surface is much more broken and uneven, it is entirely owing to the more powerful action of the streams. The frequent instances of thin horizontal strata of limestone rock appearing on both sides of a valley, corresponding in all the circumstances of elevation, thickness, and their component parts, prove that the hills have not been formed by convulsions.

With a few exceptions only, of isolated sandstone rock, the whole of this portion of the Missouri territory that I have seen is calcareous; the rocks being of a whitish limestone, containing organic remains in abundance, consisting of the casts of *Entrochii, Anomiæ,* &c. In this particular, an exception must be made to the rock forming the matrix of the lead in the mine region. In this rock I could not find any trace of organic remains whatever.

When the subterranean geography of this country shall become better known, it will probably be found to be one of the most interesting in the world. Besides the evidence furnished by the caves known to exist in the incumbent rock, there are other facts tending to prove, that, beneath the surface, there are a great many others, and of vast extent. A considerable number of the minor streams are entirely lost under ground, except in time of floods, and no place where they re-appear can be traced out. The Merrimac and Gasconade rivers have each a spring rising in their bed, either of which would be sufficient of itself to form a considerable river ; and about 300 miles S. S. W. of St. Louis, there is a branch of White River, composed entirely of one spring, so copious, that I am credibly informed a boat of thirty or forty tons burthen might sail to the source.

In many parts of this country, there are great numbers of what the inhabitants call "*sink holes.*" These are all of the same form, but differ in magnitude, some not being more than thirty yards in diameter at the top ; others exceed two hundred.

They are circular, but diminish towards the bottom, and resemble an inverted hollow cone : some of the large ones are so deep, that tall trees, growing at the bottom, cannot be seen until we approach the brink of the cavity. I have examined many of these sink holes, and in several have heard the noise of water, as of a considerable stream, running below the bottom of the cavity. In others, the subterranean stream is visible, and affords evidence that it has caused the cavity, by carrying away the incumbent earth which has fallen in from time to time.

The abundance of nitre, generated in the caves of this country, is a circumstance which ought not to be passed over unnoticed. These caves are always in the limestone rocks ; and in those which produce the nitre, the bottom is covered with earth, which is strongly impregnated with it, and visible in needle-form crystals. In order to obtain the nitre, the earth is collected and lixiviated : the water, after being saturated, is boiled down, and suffered to stand till the crystals are formed. In this manner, it is no uncommon thing for three men to make 100 lbs. of salt-petre in one day. As these caves may probably have been the resort of wild animals in former times, the accumulation of nitre, in the first instance, is not surprising ; but that the earth, on being again spread on the bottom of the cave, should be re-impregnated in the space of four or five years, is not so easily accounted for: that this is a fact, many who have been employed in making salt-petre, have assured me. In the spring of 1810, James M'Donald of Bonhomme, and his two sons, went to some caves on the Gasconade River to make salt-petre, and in a few weeks returned with 3,000 lbs. to St. Louis.

It is very probable that coal is here in great abundance. About four miles west of St. Louis, a vein, from twelve to eighteen inches in thickness, breaks out at the edge of a creek, and is used by the blacksmiths. In the year 1810, the grass of the prairie on the American Bottom, in the Illinois Territory, took fire, and kindled the dry stump of a tree, about five miles east of St. Louis: this stump set fire to a fine bed of coal on which it stood, and the coal continued to burn for several months, until the earth fell in and extinguished it. This bed breaks out at the bottom of the bluffs of the Mississippi, and is about five feet in thickness: I visited the place, and by examining the indications, found the same vein at the surface several miles distant. Near the village of St. Ferdinand, on the edge of the Missouri, the bank is one solid bed of fine coal, of unknown thickness, but certainly more than twenty feet: this bed is called by the French *La Charbonniére.*

The Lead Mines of St. Genevieve* occupy an extent of country, the limits of which have not yet been ascertained: they commence about thirty miles west of the Mississippi, and extend west and north west. That which more particularly indicates the existence of lead, is a redness of the soil, which appears to result from the decomposition of an hæmatitic iron ore, found there in great abundance, intermixed with pyrites, and in some of its states exhibiting evident proofs of being a transition from that substance. The indications are still stronger, if this earth contains sulphate of barytes, crystalized carbonate of lime, and aggregated crystals of quartz. All these are in some parts very abundant, and generally of

---

* It was the discovery of these lead mines that gave rise to the famous Mississippi scheme, projected by Law in 1719, which ruined hundreds of families in France. It was then supposed that it was a silver mine; and although the bubble burst immediately, it is surprising that Du Pratz, who wrote thirty-nine years afterwards, should still persist in the error. He not only lays down a silver mine on the Marameg in his map of Louisiana, but mentions it in his description. The Marameg is now called the Merramac, on a branch of which, called the Negro Fork, the mines of St. Genevieve are situated. Du Pratz says, " The mine of Marameg, which is silver, is pretty near the confluence of the river which gives it name; which is a great advantage to those who would work it, because they might easily, by that means, have their goods from Europe. It is situate about five hundred leagues from the sea."

a red colour, probably occasioned by the oxyde of iron contained in the soil.

These mines have been worked since about the year 1725, and until of late the ore has not been sought for in the rock, but has been found in the earth in detached lumps, intermixed with the substances mentioned above. The workmen employed, have no other implements than a pick-axe and a wooden shovel, and when at work, appear as if employed in making *tan pits*, rather than in mining. When they come to the rock, or to such a depth that it is no longer convenient to throw the dirt out of the hole, they quit, and perhaps commence a new *digging*, as they term it, within a few feet of that which they have previously abandoned. Each *digger* works separately for himself, and sells the ore to the proprietor of the soil, at two dollars per 100 lbs. It is evident from the nature of the employment, that the gain to the *diggers* must be very precarious, but in general they appear to live comfortably. They are almost all Creole French who are employed, and if I may judge from a single instance, retain as much fondness for showy dress as the most foppish of their ancestors.*

---

* On a Saturday evening I arrived at the mine *Belle Fontaine*, and employed myself until night in examining the sub-

The proprietors who buy the ore, cause it to be smelted in furnaces constructed of two parallel walls, one about eight, the other four feet high, and three and a half asunder : these are joined by two sloping side walls, and into this inclosed area the fuel and ore are thrown. In this way, they obtain from sixty to seventy per cent. of lead : the ore is said to contain eighty.

The mines belong to a number of proprietors : they are mostly held by grants from the Spanish governors formerly residing at St. Louis, and are worked with more or less spirit, as the ore happens to be abundant or otherwise, as the workmen quit one *digging* without ceremony, when they hear of better success at another. The profits of the proprietors are commensurate with the quantity of ore raised on their property : therefore, when the *diggings* become less productive than usual, they make trials on different parts of their land, to discover where the ore is more abundant, that the *diggers* may be induced to remain with them. These trials consist in nothing more than

---

stances thrown out by the *diggers*, and found the most interesting specimens amongst the refuse of one man, who, on that account, I particularly noticed. On the following morning I met him in the village, dressed in a white gown, with red slippers, and a blue silk waistcoat, embroidered with silver lace.

digging a hole in some part of the woods, to the depth of three or four feet, and judging by the quantity of ore *(Galena)* what degree of success may be expected.

A little time before I visited Richwood Mines, the property of Monsieur Lebaume, of St. Louis, he had made forty trials, by simply digging holes, not more than four feet deep, in places remote from each other, on his land. In thirty-eight of these he found ore, and from one hole more than half a cwt. was raised. This gentleman owns a square league.

As soon as any particular district is found so abundant as to warrant a furnace to be erected near it, they give it a name. Whilst I was at St. Louis, one of these places was discovered, and named *Mine au Shibboleth*, from which, I was credibly informed, four millions of pounds weight of ore was raised in this manner in one summer. The *diggings* which I visited were *Mine au Burton, Mine Belle Fontaine, Richwood Mines, Old Diggings, New Diggings,* and *Elliot's Diggings.* Some of these *diggings* are ten or twelve miles distant from each other. *Mine la Motte,* on the waters of the river St. Francis, is thirty or forty miles south of all the rest. Some of these mines have fallen into the hands of Americans, who have ventured to penetrate the rock, which is always found at a depth of from six to twelve feet below the surface, and have been amply rewarded for their enterprize.

I remained a few days with Mr. Elliot, who at that time had only just commenced on the rock, but had the most promising prospects of success. He had raised a considerable quantity of ore, and many tons of *blende*, and with the last had repaired the road to his works, not knowing what substance it was. Mr. Moses Austin, proprietor of *Mine au Burton*, had been very successful, having found large masses of ore in the caves of the rock into which he had penetrated.

At the *New Diggings* a great deal had been raised out of the rock, and a considerable quantity was lying on the bank in very large lumps. When I visited that place, they were impeded by water, and had no better means of getting rid of it, than those which buckets, raised by a windlass, afforded. I was prevented from descending by the quantity of water then in the mine.

Although the district of country which contains the present *diggings*, is considered as comprising the mines, I am of opinion that the lead extends to a very great distance beyond those limits. I have seen all the indications on the upper part of the Merrimac River, fifty or sixty miles west of the present workings, and still farther to the northward, at the mouth of the Gasconade, on the Missouri. It is supposed by some that it extends to the mines belonging to the Saukee and Fox nations of Indians, which are situated on the Mississippi, six hundred miles above St. Louis.—These mines are known to extend over a space of eighty miles in length, and nine miles in breadth.*

---

* These mines are of great value to the Saukee and Fox nations. As the game on the lands which they claim is nearly destroyed, they have therefore been compelled to commence the business of mining, or rather digging. The ore is raised by the men, but the operation of smelting is done by the squaws. The method by which they extract the metal was described to me by Mr. Prior, who was of Messrs. Lewis and Clarke's party, and who traded with these Indians for lead. They first dug a deep cavity in the ground, near a perpendicular bank of the Mississippi, and from the face of the bank make an horizontal hole to meet the bottom of it. A quantity of dry wood is then thrown into the cavity, and set fire to, after which the ore is thrown in, and the supply of both continued. The metal runs out at the horizontal opening, and is received in holes made by the Indians with their heels in the sand of the river. In this state it is bought by the traders from St. Louis, who afterwards cast it into pigs in their own moulds. Formerly, these Indians gave permission to a person of the name of Dubuque to dig lead: he resided at their village, being much respected by them, and acquired some property, the management of which, after his death,

Some of the isolated sand-stone rocks in this territory, alluded to, are remarkable for their purity, being so white as to exactly resemble the purest lump sugar. These would furnish an excellent material for the manufacture of glass.

About five miles west of Herculaneum, which is situated on the Mississippi, thirty miles below St. Louis, there is a limestone rock, about a quar-

---

fell into the hands of Augustus Choutou, of St. Louis, who, in 1810, advertised for sale Dubuque's property in the mines, or his right of digging lead. It was bought by Colonel Smith, the proprietor of *Mine Belle Fontaine,* and Mr. Moorhead of St. Louis, for about 3000 dollars. They ascended the Mississippi with an armed party, to take possession, but were very roughly handled by the Indians, and happy in having escaped with their lives. The Indians immediately afterwards called a council, and being fearful of giving offence to the American government, they sent deputies to St. Louis, to plead their cause before Governor Howard and General Clarke, who performed their mission with great ability; first disclaiming any intention to continue the grant beyond the life of Dubuque, and, secondly, any wish to offend the government of the United States, by driving away Smith and Moorhead. They next stated, that when the *Great Spirit* gave the land to the Red Men, their ancestors, he foresaw that the White Men would come into the country, and that the game would be destroyed; therefore, out of his great goodness, he put lead into the ground, that they, their wives and children, might continue to exist: they lastly appealed to the justice of their *Great Father,* the President of the United States. Governor Howard and General Clarke approved of their conduct, and assured them of the protection of the government.

ter of a mile in length, and in some parts forty or fifty feet high. This rock is so completely perforated in almost every part, as to resemble a honeycomb, and the perforations are from one-eighth to three quarters of an inch in diameter. It has exactly the appearance of marine rocks, perforated by *Mytilus lithophagus*, or *Rugosus*.

Fossil bones have been dug up in various places in Upper Louisiana. At a salt lick, about three miles from the Merrimac river, and twelve from St. Louis, several bones have been discovered, evidently belonging to the same species of mammoth as those found on the Ohio, and in Orange County, State of New York. I have frequently been informed of a place on Osage river, where there are abundance of bones, of great magnitude. General Clarke shewed me a tooth brought from the interior: it was a grinder, and belonged to the animal mentioned by Cuvier, called by him Mastodonté *Avec dents carrés.*

The general character of this country is that of prairie, with scattered trees, and interspersed clumps. On the summits of the ridges, the timber is generally red cedar, *(Juniperus virginiana)* on the prairie, post oak, *(Quercus obtusiloba)* black jack, *(Quercus nigra)* black walnut, *(Juglans nigra)* and shell bark hickory, *(Juglans squamosa.)*

The alluvion of the rivers contain a greater variety, of which the principal are—cotton wood, *(Populus angulosa)* sycamore, *(Platanus occidentalis)* over-cup oak, *(Quercus macrocarpa)* nettle tree, or hackberry, *(Celtis crassifolia)* hoop ash, *(Celtis occidentalis)* honey locust, *(Gleditsia triacanthos)* black locust, *(Robinia pseudacacia)* coffee tree, *(Guilandina dioica)* peccan, *(Juglans olivæformis)* and many of the trees common in the states east of the Alleghanies.*

The soil is generally excellent, being for the most part black loam, and is tilled without much trouble.

The climate is very fine: the spring commences about the middle of March in the neighbourhood of St. Louis, at which time the willow, *(Salix)* the elm, *(Ulmus Americana)* and maples, *(Acer rubrum* and *Saccharinum)* are in flower. The spring rains usually occur in May, after which month the weather continues fine, almost without interruption, until September, when rain again occurs about the equinox, after which it remains again fine serene weather until near Christmas, when the winter commences. About the begin-

---

* A list of some of the herbaceous plants of the Missouri territory will be found annexed.

ning or middle of October the Indian summer* commences, and is immediately known by the change which takes place in the atmosphere, as it now becomes hazy, or what they term smoky. This gives to the sun a red appearance, and takes away the glare of light, so that all the day, except a few hours about noon, he may be looked at with the naked eye without pain : the air is perfectly quiescent and all is stillness, as if nature, after her exertions during the summer, were now at rest. The winters are sharp, but it may be remarked that less snow falls, and they are much more moderate on the west than on the east side of the Alleghanies in similar latitudes.

The wild productions of the Missouri Territory, such as fruits, nuts, and berries, are numerous : of these the summer grape *(Vitis æstivalis)* appears to be the most valuable, as the French have made a considerable quantity of wine from it by collecting the wild fruit.† This species grows in abundance on the prairies, and produces a profusion of fine

---

* Indians begin to provide for the winter when this state of the weather commences, as they know it will soon approach.

† Mr. James Berry, with whom I resided, about four miles from St. Louis, told me that he made eight quarts of wine from the grapes of one of these vines, which ran up a small tree, about 150 yards from his house.

bunches. The winter grape *(Vitis vulpinum)* is remarkable for the large size of its vine, which climbs to the tops of the highest trees, and takes such full possession of their tops, that after the fall of the leaf, the tree to which it has attached itself seems to be loaded with fruit. The vine at the bottom is commonly six or eight inches in diameter. I measured one near the Merrimac river, that was thirty-seven inches in circumference near the ground, after which it divided into three branches, each branch taking possession of a tree. The fruit is very good after the frosts have commenced. Another fruit found here is the persimon, *(Diospyros virginiana)* which in appearance resembles a plum, excepting that the permanent calyx of the flower remains. It is so astringent until ameliorated by the frosts, that on being eaten, it draws up the mouth, and when swallowed, contracts the throat in such a manner as to cause a sensation similar to that of choking.

The papaw *(Anona triloba)* is found in plenty on the alluvion of the rivers. The fruit is of the magnitude and shape of a middling sized cucumber, and grows in clusters of three, four, or five together : when ripe the pulp is of the consistence of a custard, and is very agreeable to some palates ; but the hogs will not touch them. Strawberries are in vast abundance on the prairies, and are very fine. The pecan, or Illinois nut, is a kind

of walnut, but very different from all the other
species, both in the form and texture of its shell,
which is so thin as to be cracked between the teeth
with the greatest ease. It is of an oblong form,
and from that circumstance the tree which produces
it has obtained the name of *Juglans olivæformis.*
There are several other species of hickory and walnut, which yield nuts in great abundance. These,
together with acorns from the various species of
oak, furnish abundance of food for hogs.

The quadrupeds found in parts inhabited by the
whites, of which the flesh is eaten, are bear, deer,
hares, racoon, opossum, and a variety of squirrels.
With bear, deer, and turkeys, the town of St. Louis
is frequently supplied by a tribe of the Shawanee
nation of Indians, who live about seventy miles
west of that place. They usually charge a quarter
of a dollar for a turkey or a quarter of venison.

It is necessary to observe that Upper Louisiana
was settled from Canada, not by way of Orleans,
but by proceeding along the Lakes, and descending the Illinois or Miami rivers, and may be considered as a distinct colony, the history of which,
so far as may be gathered from themselves, does
not present those horrid examples of treachery and
injustice to the Indians, which will for ever dis-
grace the memory of those who first formed the

lower settlement. The consequence has been, that although individual acts of injustice or aggression, committed against the Indians, have met with due and appropriate punishment, yet no general act has been committed of a nature so atrocious as to provoke general extermination; a thing extremely easy to have been effected by the Indians in the early part of the settlement, as there were several powerful tribes in their vicinity. The inhabitants of Kaskaskias say that it was coeval with Philadelphia, and the common term for Vincennes, (Old Post) shows that it must have been one of the first settlements, if not the first. Both these are on the east side of the Mississippi, as also are Cahokia and the small settlement of Prairie du Roche. Besides these four, on the west side, there were five villages originally settled, each of which, besides its proper name, has a nick-name given to it. St. Genevieve is *Misère;* Carondolet, *Vuide Poche;* St. Louis, *Pain Court;* St. Ferdinand, *Florissante;* and St. Charles, *Petit Cote.* These nine villages were scattered some more than 100 miles distant from each other, and no two of them were so situated as to be capable of rendering mutual aid, in case of attack from the Indians, and for more than sixty years five of them existed, isolated in a wilderness, 600 miles at least from any other white settlers.

The villages were regularly laid out in squares

of 300 feet on each side, the houses standing towards the streets, and the interior of the area composed of gardens and orchards. To each of these villages was appropriated a large space of ground, and fenced in the form of a parallelogram. In this space allotments are laid out, correspondent in number and relative magnitude with the town lots. These allotments extend the whole length of the field; but their magnitude is determined by the breadth, which is marked on one of the fences, being once, or once and a half, or twice, &c. the length of the side of a square arpent of land. In the common field belonging to Carondolet, these narrow stripes are more than a mile and a half in length. Besides the appropriation of land for cultivation, an extensive tract was laid out for each town as a forest, or demesne, from which each individual cuts what wood he thinks proper. All these appropriations have been ratified by the commissioners appointed by the government of the United States, since the cession of Louisiana, to examine into claims. The French, who are the descendants of the first settlers, are very indolent, and so much attached to the manners of their ancestors, and even their practices in husbandry, that although they see their American neighbours, by the application of improved implements and methods, able to cultivate double the quantity of ground in the same time, nothing can induce them to abandon

their old practices : and if any one attempts to reason with them on the subject, their constant reply
is, "As it was good enough for our forefathers, it
is good enough for us ;" whence it appears that
even veneration for ancestry may become an evil.
They cultivate maize, wheat, oats, barley, beans,
(*Phaseolus*) pumpkins, water and musk melons,
and tobacco and cotton for their own use. Apples
and peaches are very fine : the former abundant,
and do not require to be engrafted. They pay
great attention to gardening, and have a good assortment of roots and vegetables. Notwithstand-
their want of industry, there is an appearance of
comfort and independence in their villages, as,
from the richness of the soil, and fineness of the
climate, the labours attendant on agriculture, and
attention necessary to their cattle, are comparatively trivial. They have abundance of horses,
cows, and hogs, all which run at large on the
prairies, as they have no inclosures but for the
purpose of agriculture. They mow a little grass
on the prairie, which they make into hay, and give
it to their horses and cattle when the ground is covered with snow : at other times they leave them
to provide for themselves. The hogs sustain themselves on strawberries, hazle nuts, hickory nuts,
acorns and roots, and must be occasionally sought
for in the woods, to prevent them from becoming
entirely wild. On these occasions, the proprietor

fills his saddle bags with the ears of Indian corn, with which he mounts his horse, generally with his rifle on his shoulder. If he finds them within three or four miles of his house, he thinks himself fortunate; but it sometimes happens that he is two days in "hunting them up," as they term it. When he finds them, he throws down an ear of corn, which they devour, and he rides gently towards home, with the whole herd screaming after him. When they are almost inclined to give up the chase, he throws down another ear, which practice he continues until he brings them into his yard, where he shuts them up, and feeds them. Here they remain until the morning, when he again feeds them, marks the young pigs, sets them at liberty, and probably does not see them again for a fortnight or three weeks. That each planter may identify his own hogs, he marks them in the ear, and in each township an office is established, in which these marks are registered; they are either holes or slits, or both, differently arranged; so that no two marks are alike; and it is against the laws of the territory to expose the carcase of a hog for sale without having the ears upon it.

St. Louis, the capital of this territory, is very pleasantly situated on the Mississippi, about eighteen miles below the mouth of the Missouri, in latitude 38° 5′ and longitude 89° 55′ W. It has a decided advantage over any of the other towns, on account of its being situated on a rock, but little elevated above the high floods of the river, and immediately on its border. Such situations are very rare, as the Mississippi is almost universally bounded either by high perpendicular rocks or loose alluvial soil, the latter of which is in continual danger of being washed away by the annual floods, to such an extent, that a whole plantation, situated on the border of the river, has been known to have been swept away during one flood. Fort Chartres, erected at a vast expence by the French government on the border of the river, prior to the cession of Louisiana in 1763, is now almost entirely swept away. The fur trade of the Mississippi and the Missouri, together with that of the tributary streams, almost wholly centers in this town; and after the return of Messrs. Lewis and Clark from the Pacific Ocean, a fur company was formed, for the purpose of trading with the nations on the head waters of the Missouri, which, from a variety of untoward events, but principally from the hostile and bloody disposition of the Indians, has miscarried.

There is no part of the western country that holds out greater advantages to the new settler than the Missouri Territory. It is inferior to no

part in point of soil or climate, and has a decided
advantage over the country on the Ohio, as the
transit to Orleans may be made at any season of
the year, whereas the Ohio is not navigable during
the months of August, September, and October.
It is also from 600 to 1000 miles nearer to that
city than the upper part of the Ohio. Opportunities of purchasing settlements or plantations, already
formed, are very frequent, and at very moderate
terms, as the rage of retiring back prevails here in
as great a degree as in the other new countries.
Wild land, as it is here called, may either be had
from the government of the United States, or from
the old French inhabitants, several of whom possess very large tracts, obtained by grants from the
Spanish governors. The titles of these lands are
now undoubted, as they have been ratified by the
commissioners appointed by the government of the
United States to examine into claims. The price
of land is various, but may frequently be obtained
on better terms from the land owners than from
the government, or for less than two dollars per acre.
In the reclaiming of wild land, or the forming of a
plantation from a state of nature, the trouble and
labour is much less than in clearing a forest, as here
the trees are not more abundant on the upland
than would be necessary for fuel and for fences.
They naturally stand at a sufficient distance from
each other to admit a fine undergrowth of grass

and herbage. This country, as well as the western region, will reap incalculable benefit from the application of steam boats on the Mississippi. Of these a great many are now building in the different ports of the Ohio. This mode of conveyance will also be much facilitated by the abundance of excellent coal so universally spread over these regions.

It is necessary to observe, that what has been stated relative to the climate, duration of winter, agriculture, &c. &c. relates more particularly to the region included betwixt the mouths of the Ohio and Missouri, or from 37 to $39\frac{1}{2}$ degrees of latitude; but this territory extends from 29 to 50 degrees, and therefore proper allowances must be made for the differences of latitude. In an agricultural point of view, it may be divided into three regions, suitable for the culture of as many great staple articles, viz. sugar, cotton, and corn. The sugar region reaches from the coast to latitude 31 or $31\frac{1}{2}$ degrees: the culture of sugar only commenced about 15 years ago, and until of late has been confined to the alluvion of the Mississippi; but there is an extensive tract, suitable for that culture, lying west of that river, and reaching to the Sabine river, comprehending the countries of the Oppelousas and Atacapas, which is now settling fast, and in point of soil can scarcely be equalled. In the year 1811, some of the plantations on the Mississippi produced as much as 500 hogsheads of sugar ; and the cultivation is rapidly encreasing, as many of the planters have already made immense fortunes.

The region proper for the cultivation of cotton, and too cold for that of the sugar-cane, extends from 31½ to about 36 degrees of latitude : the species cultivated is *Gossypium annuum.* It will grow many degrees north of 36 ; but will not yield a sufficient crop, nor is the cotton so good, for the following reasons :—of the pods containing the cotton, the terminal pods of the principal branches are the first ripe : the next in succession are those of the secondary branches, which are followed by those of the tertiary ones, &c. &c.; but in each successive generation, the number is increased in something like the ratio of a geometrical progression. In the northerly part of the cotton region, the winter comes on before the cotton in the pods on the lateral branches is ripe, and a great portion of the crop is destroyed, which a few degrees further south would have been ripened. But the avarice of some planters prompts them to continue the gathering of their crops too long, and the quality of their cotton is deteriorated thereby, as the sun is too feeble to give the last part of their crop sufficient strength. The culture of the cotton plant is not attended with much trouble. The seeds are planted from 3 to 3½ feet asunder ; and after the plants have acquired a little strength, they are weeded and earthed up : no further care is required until the gathering of the pods commences. The cotton is then separated from the seeds by a machine, called the *saw gin.* *

---

* From observation I am led to believe that the staple of cotton is sometimes injured in the gin ; and as this machine is now universally used to separate the cotton from the seed, I shall describe it. The saws are circular, about six or eight inches in diameter, they are made of thin steel plate, and are toothed like those used for cutting wood, excepting that they make a more acute angle with the radii. Twenty-four, thirty, thirty-six, or more of these saws are placed on an iron shaft, at about one inch asunder. This shaft is fixed in a frame, three feet, or three feet six inches high, and parallel to it is placed a trough, not unlike a manger. One side of the trough is composed of thin plates of iron, exceeding in number that of the saws by one. This admits one of these plates betwixt each two saws, and they are so near each other as barely to admit the saw to pass between them. A fourth part of the saw works within the trough. Beneath the saws a cylindrical brush turns the same way, but with greater velocity. On the end of the shaft on which the saws are there is a fast and a loose pulley for driving the machine, with a belt for stopping it at pleasure. When the gin is intended to be set to work, a quantity of cotton, as taken from the pods, is thrown into the trough, and the belt is put on the fast pulley. The saws, in passing through the troughs, continue to load their teeth with cotton, which is instantly thrown off by the brush, and in a few minutes nothing remains in the trough but bare seeds. The management of this gin is mostly committed to negroes, who, anxious to finish their task, drive the machine with too great velocity, by which, I conceive, not only the staple of the cotton

As there are public gins established almost in every part, to which a planter may take his cotton, and have it cleaned and packed on moderate terms, it is in the power of a poor man to turn cotton-planter ; and if he has a numerous family, so much the better, as females, and even children, can be employed in gathering the pods, and in taking the cotton from them. If he settles on wild land, he can enter upon the culture of cotton with more facility than on any other crop, as the ground requires less preparation.

This part of Louisiana as yet contains but very few white settlers, although, for the most part, the soil is excellent, and the climate charming. Two very large rivers, Red River and the Arkansas, enter the Mississippi in this region, and run their whole course through it : they are both navigable to the confines of the internal provinces of New Mexico, and furnish to those parts the best means of communication with the ocean. Of these means, when Mexico shall break its chain, it will avail itself, and this will become one of the richest and most valuable parts of the United States.

---

is injured, but the green lumps, which are in fact the abortive seeds, are broken, and carried through along with the cotton. From this cause, in a great measure, arises the difference of quality of cotton from the same plantation.

In an agricultural point of view, the vast tract
of prairie extending through all these regions, is
an important object of consideration. Amongst
intelligent Americans, the question of—whether it
can or cannot be peopled by civilized man? has
often been agitated. Accustomed, as they are, to
a profusion of timber, for buildings, fuel, and
fences, they are not aware of the small quantity of
that article which may be dispensed with, in a
country abounding in another substance for fuel;
nor can they conceive, that fences, and even buildings, may be constructed with the application of a
very small portion of timber. Under these impressions, the belief in America is, that the prairie cannot be inhabited by the whites; even Mr. Brackenridge says it cannot be cultivated. My own opinion is, that it can be cultivated; and that, in process of time, it will not only be peopled and cultivated, but that it will be one of the most beautiful
countries in the world.

If I may be permitted to judge from travelling
nearly 500 miles through it, I must pronounce the
soil to be excellent, and in almost every part where
I saw it in a state of nature, it was covered with
the finest verdure imaginable. The stratum immediately below the vegetable soil is almost universally a very tenacious clay, and extremely well
calculated to form a material for brick, or, in the

first instance, for such habitations as are made in Ireland, many of which are very comfortable. In time timber would be raised; for to suppose it would not grow there because it does not, would be absurd. Whenever this region shall commence to be peopled, the first settlements will be made at the edge of the woody region, or on the borders of the rivers, where a little timber may be found, and probably the first wave in the tide of population will be formed of shepherds and herdsmen. The tacit compact mutually binding betwixt man and the animals he domesticates, implies a duty connected with an interest to both parties. Man furnishes to them food and protection, and enables them to pass a few years of comfortable existence: they repay him with their lives or their services. In all cases, the domestication of animals is of the most value to man in those parts where he can perform his duty to them at the least expence to himself. In no part of the world can it be done with less trouble than in the southern part of this region. A convincing proof of this is, that here domesticated animals have dissolved the contract, and that thousands and tens of thousands of their descendants still maintain their independence. If, besides yielding food and protection to herbivorous animals, other means of reducing them to a state of dependence on man could not be found, domestication without inclosures (which imply coercion) would be in these parts impracticable, because food is at all times in abundance, and the want of protection would be obviated by an association in numbers. But salt furnishes those means, by the aid of which the shepherd or the herdsman obtains a complete dominion over the will of his flock or his herds, and in the midst of this vast region can call them round him at pleasure.*

I shall close this article by a few observations on the state of this country before it was transferred to the United States, and of the immense value and importance it is to that government. If a person who visited this country, and witnessed its fertility, did not at the same time witness the want of industry and enterprise in the descendants of the old inhabitants, he would be surprised that its ad-

---

* In a fertile country, and when not circumscribed by fences, there is a continued tendency in animals to return to the state of nature. Besides the accounts of others tending to prove this, I had evidence of it in my horse, on the prairie near St. Louis, in the summer of 1810. He was usually remarkably docile, and although there was not a single fence to obstruct his passage to the Pacific Ocean, he was easily caught when often wanted : but during the time I was attacked by the ague, sometimes he was not sought for during a fortnight. At those times he would let no one come near him, and shewed an utter contempt for corn, when offered to him ; but a display of salt was at all times a temptation too great to be resisted, and he quietly resigned his liberty.

vancement towards improvement has been so slow. But besides this, the political circumstances under which it has been placed, have been such as to preclude any possibility of prosperity; as the very nature and design of the principles by which it was governed, whilst under the dominion of Spain, was to prevent it. The invariable policy of that government, as regards her colonies, is to prevent, as much as possible, all intercourse betwixt them and other nations; and anxious only to raise *immediate* revenue, it is in the continued habit of sacrificing futurity to the present. The governors were petty tyrants, who considered their situations as the means only of aggrandizing themselves; to which as well as the interest of the province, that of the Spanish government, must always give way. Anxious only to enrich themselves, and vested with almost unlimited power, the interest or prosperity of the colony was an object of very remote consideration. The most depressing regulations were made to shackle the internal trade of the country; no man could sell the smallest article, not even a row of pins, without a licence, and those licences were sold at the most extravagant rates. A stranger coming into the province, and offering goods at a fair price, was certain to be sent to prison, and to have his goods confiscated. All favours from these governors, all grants of land, or even common privileges, could only be obtained by bribery. Some of the governors, not satisfied with the fruit of their rapacious exactions on the province, were guilty of the most shameful acts of villany towards their own government. A little above St. Louis stands a small triangular fort, which, I was assured by one of the old settlers, was built by the inhabitants without one shilling of expense to the governor; who rewarded some by grants of land, and others by certain privileges; and, for building this fort, a bill was sent in to the Spanish government to a large amount, which was paid.*

---

* Schultz relates the following anecdote in his travels, which proves that the above instance is not a solitary one :—

" At the lower end of the town of St. Genevieve, the remains ot a Spanish fort are still to be seen, which, being erected on an eminence, corresponded with that of Kaskaskias by signals.

" It seems after the fort was completed, the commandant had to wait upon the governor of the province to present his charges. They were accordingly presented, and amounted to 421 dollars. The governor, after examining the account, returned it to the commandant, informing him there was some mistake. The commandant retired and examined it again ; but finding it entirely correct, presented it once more. The governor, on looking it over, informed him it was still incorrect, and advised him to consult with some friend, as he had omitted a figure or two. The commandant then called upon a friend to look over his accounts with him, who no sooner saw the amount than he burst into a loud laugh, and taking up a pen, added an 0 to the sum already stated. The commandant presented his accounts a third time, when his excellency replied that it was not quite right yet. The commandant was amazed : but what was his astonishment,

Under so detestable a system of government the energies of man must for ever remain dormant, and the most fertile regions eternally unproductive to the world.

The political and commercial advantages that will arise to the United States from the acquisition of Louisiana are incalculable, besides the vast revenue that will arise from the sale of lands. The exclusive right to the Mississippi river is an object of the highest importance. The acquisition of the sugar region alone would have sufficiently indemnified the American government. But without considering the positive advantages that will arise to the United States from the possession of Louisiana, the evils that might, and would have arisen from its being in the possession of another power, which could have maintained the dominion of the Mississippi, are also incalculable. The most prominent of these evils would have been the separation of the States west of the Alleghanies from the Union, as, without the free navigation of the Mississippi, the products of their fertile soil must have perished on their hands for

---

when he related the affair to his friend, to see him add another 0 to the last sum, making it 42,100 instead of 421 ! On presenting the account the fourth time, it was graciously received, and for the discharge of the whole a very small part was paid to the commandant."

the want of a market. So far is a navigable river from being a boundary calculated to prevent collision betwixt two different states, that it affords the greatest possible opportunities for invasion or predatory excursions; and in case of war with the power possessing Louisiana, a line of more than 2,000 miles in length of the United States would have been subject to be invaded in half an hour after the enemy left his own territory. But besides the devastations incident on regular warfare, this extended border would have been subject to the depredations of the various tribes of warlike Indians residing west of the Mississippi, who would have been a terrible engine in the hands of the power possessing the dominion of that country. In a state of hostility, they would have rendered the eastern bank of the Mississippi wholly uninhabitable.

REMARKS

ON

THE STATES OF OHIO, KENTUCKY, AND INDIANA,

WITH

THE ILLINOIS AND WESTERN TERRITORY,

AND ON THE

EMIGRATIONS TO THOSE COUNTRIES.

In a tour across the Alleghanies, and through the regions west of these mountains and east of the Mississippi river, I did not keep a regular journal, but contented myself with making general remarks, without any expectation that they would ever be submitted to public view. From these remarks I shall briefly extract such matter as may be useful to those who wish to visit the western country, or be read with interest by those who do not.

The committee appointed by the government of the United States, in the year 1816, to examine into the state of American manufactures, in speaking of the western country, say, "The rapidity of its growth is such, that even whilst we are employed in drawing the portrait, the features continue to en-

large, and the picture becomes distorted." As
nothing can be more true than the above observation, it is therefore evident that a traveller, in speaking of this country as acted upon by the operations
of man, can only speak with confidence of *what
was*. It is only on its natural formation that he can
speak of *what is* as far as is known.

The region to which these observations will more
particularly apply, is bounded by the Alleghanies
to the south-east, by the Mississippi on the west,
and the Great Lakes to the north. The Kaatskill
mountains, on the Hudson river, about 130 miles
from New York, are considered as the northern
termination of the chain of mountains called the
Alleghanies, from which point they proceed in a
south-west direction to the Floridas, a distance of
900 miles, and parallel with the general direction
of the Atlantic coast. The country west of this
chain is in so many points of view different from
that comprehended betwixt it and the Atlantic, as
to demand a separate and distinct description. As
almost the whole of the population of this country
is confined to the vicinity of the Ohio or its tributary streams, the portion which furnishes water to
that river will first be considered. West and north-
west there is a vast tract on which that river is not
dependent. That tract, as regards its natural for-

mation, has a distinct character, which will also be particularly noticed.

The Ohio, from Pittsburgh to its mouth, is supposed to be 1188 miles in length, and receives in its course a considerable number of streams, of which the following are the principal :—

Tennessee,	Sciota,
Cumberland,	Big Sandy River,
Green River,	Great Kenhawa,
Salt River,	Little Kenhawa,
Kentucky River,	Muskingum,
Little Miami,	Wabash.
Great Miami,	

Its name Ohio is of Indian origin, and signifies beautiful. The French have not adopted the term, but call it in their maps of this country *La Belle Rivière.* Although only a small stream when compared to the Mississippi, some idea of its magnitude may be formed by those who are only accustomed to see rivers in miniature, by examining the following statement of the area from which it derives its waters :—

T

	Sqr. Miles.
Illinois Territory, $\frac{1}{10}$,	5,200
Indiana Territory (the whole),	37,050
State of Ohio, $\frac{4}{5}$,	35,088
Pennsylvania, $\frac{1}{3}$,	16,493
New York, $\frac{1}{100}$,	521
Maryland, $\frac{1}{100}$,	140
Virginia, $\frac{2}{5}$,	28,200
North Carolina, $\frac{1}{50}$,	1,100
South Carolina, $\frac{1}{150}$,	152
Georgia, $\frac{1}{30}$,	2,000
Kentucky (the whole),	40,110
Tennessee, $\frac{3}{4}$,	32,400
Square miles,	198,464

The area of England and Wales is 49,450 square miles : it therefore appears that this river receives the water of a surface four times that éxtent. This surface is comprehended betwixt the parallels of 35 and 43 degrees of latitude ; a climate perhaps the best on the globe as regards the comforts of man.

The seasons and general state of the weather correspond with what has been mentioned of Upper Louisiana in similar latitudes :—in spring heavy rains; in summer an almost cloudless sky, with heavy dews at night; in autumn some rain, followed by the *Indian summer ;* and the winter from ten weeks to three months long, which is dry, sharp, and pleasant.

From the Alleghanies to the Lakes there are no mountains, or scarcely an elevation deserving the name of a hill, the bluffs which border the rivers excepted. It is nevertheless relieved from the dull monotony of a level plain by numberless valleys, through which the streams flow, and by small elevations, termed ridges. The soil is much superior to that of the countries east of the Alleghanies, and varies in quality. These variations are denoted by the term first, second, and third rate. In the early stage of the transition of a fertile country from a state of nature to that of improvement and the arts, but little can be known as respects its geological formation, or, in other words, what it may contain as regards minerals. In general the first settlers are only cultivators of the soil, and never examine to any considerable depth below the surface, excepting by digging wells. All that is known of this country on those subjects has been discovered in that way, or has manifested itself on the surface, and is confined, as regards useful articles, to coal, salt, iron, lead, and nitre. From the numerous and general indications, and the known existence of coal, it may be presumed to be very abundant. In examining the beds of most of the rivers, rounded nodules of coal may be found mixed with the stones and gravel, and beds of argillaceous schist, containing vegetable impressions, are frequent : in some instances these beds contain masses of pyrites.

T 2

Coal is actually found at Pittsburgh, at Zanesville, on Green River, in the Illinois, and in the western territories. It is uniformly bituminous, and highly charged with that substance.* In all these instances it has manifested itself on the surface of the earth, and indicates almost inexhaustible beds.

Salt, the most useful article at present, is found in various places, but as yet only in a state of solution, and has mostly been indicated by the excavations made by wild animals before the country was discovered by the whites. These, and in particular those of the herbivorous kind, have a strong predilection for salt. They resorted in immense numbers to every place where a salt spring existed, and not only drank the water, but licked up all the earth in its vicinity, which was impregnated with saline particles. Some of these excavations are of a surprising extent, when the means by which they have been effected is considered. That which led to the discovery of the salt spring called the Ohio Saline, about twenty miles from the mouth of the Wabash, is several acres in extent, and from six to

---

* This fact is remarkable in a geological point of view, when connected with another, which is, that almost all, if not the whole of the coal discovered east of the Alleghanies, is of the kind called by Kirwan mineral carbon, containing no bitumen. Vast beds of this description of coal exist on the Susquehannah and Delaware rivers. It contains 90 per cent. of carbon.

ten feet in depth. On viewing these, and contemplating the length of time necessary for such a mass of earth to be carried away in the stomachs of animals, the mind is struck with astonishment.* The existence of salt on the Kenhawa was not pointed out by these indications. On sinking a well, they came to a red sandstone rock before they had obtained a sufficiency of water, and perforated the rock, when the salt water immediately issued up with great force. This rock is now found to extend for several miles on both sides of the river. Wherever it is perforated salt water is found beneath, and several works for the manufacture of salt are already established.†

---

* Salt is made at various places in the western country, and the manufacture is rapidly increasing. The principal establishments are on the Kenhawa, at Bullet's and at Mann's Licks, Kentucky, and at the Ohio Saline, at the mouth of the Wabash.

† In passing down that river I had an opportunity of seeing the manner in which they construct their wells for the salt water, which, on account of its singularity, I shall describe. They first ascertain by boring at what depth they shall come to the rock, and afterwards look out for a hollow tree, which must be at least from three to four feet in diameter. This they cut down carefully for fear of splitting, and saw off such a length as will reach from the surface of the ground to the rock. If the hollow of the tree is not large enough to allow room sufficient for a man to work within, they enlarge it. A well is next dug, and when so deep that there is danger of the earth falling in, the trunk is put down, and sunk to the surface of the rock. After the influx of fresh water is prevented by calkings round the edges at the

Iron ore is found in many places, but chiefly in the neighbourhood where foundries have been esta-

---

bottom of the trunk, the perforation is made, and the salt water immediately rises to the surface. Besides the use here mentioned, hollow trees were applied to other purposes, being cut across in different lengths, and used by the first settlers as tubs to hold grain, &c. Any portion so cut off is called a gum, a name probably arising from the almost exclusive application of the gum trees to these purposes; for although many species of trees are liable to become hollow, yet none are so perfectly hollowed as the gum tree *(Liquidamber styraciflua.)* These trees, as I am informed, are often found so completely hollow as to leave the sound part not more than an inch in thickness, and the inside surface perfectly smooth.

Having mentioned the Kenhawa, I must observe, that on arriving at the falls of that river, ninety miles from the Ohio. I found a boat going from thence to Kenhawa Court-house, with some goods that had been brought over the Alleghanies. A passage was cheerfully granted to me, during which I enquired for the burning well, and expressed a wish to see it. The boatmen informed me it was four miles from the river, and it would not be convenient for them to wait until I visited it, but promised to show me what would equally gratify my curiosity. Accordingly, near the edge of the river, and about fifteen miles farther down, they landed, and conducted me to where there was a hole dug in the sandy bank of the river, about a foot in diameter. From this hole a flame issued at least two feet high. Several stones were placed round the margin, on which some other boatmen had set their kettles to cook their meat. I had noticed for several miles above a vein of iron ore appearing at the surface, about the height of the highest floods, and in almost every part of the bank great quantities of ochre. The same appearances continued to the distance of several miles below. From noticing this circumstance, I was led to form a conjecture on the formation of

blished. About fourteen miles west of the Ohio
Saline, in the Illinois Territory, there is a lead
mine, which was discovered by a gentleman from
Tennessee, of the name of Guest. It is not yet
worked, but seems to promise well. Some small
excavations have been made, and a quantity of
galena found. It appears to have no connection or
affinity with the mines of St. Genevieve, not only
on account of the distance being about 150 miles,
but from the marked difference in the rock which
is the matrix of the ore, and in the substances
which are concomitant with it. The rock in this
mine is of that species of limestone called ketton-
stone, or compact limestone of Kirwan, and consists of very small accreted round granulations.
The ore is mixed with beautiful fluor spar, of several colours, as blue, brown, yellow, and pellucid.
The caves yielding salt-petre are still more abundant than those of Upper Louisiana, or rather they
are better known, and some of them are of surprising extent. They abound chiefly on Green, Tennessee, and Cumberland rivers.

---

the gas that supplied the flame, and was persuaded that there is
a vast body of iron ore, which, from the appearance of so much
ochre, is in a continued state of oxydization, and produces a
constant decomposition of water, with the oxygen of which it
unites, and consequently a quantity of hydrogen is evolved.—
May not this be the cause?

The country is generally calcareous ; but many rocks of freestone occur. One producing excellent flags may be observed near the place where the battle was fought at Point Pleasant, on the Kenhawa.

Near the mouth of Cabin Creek, about six miles above Limestone, on the Ohio, there is a hill almost covered with detached petrified casts of marine shells, in which a great many species may be observed.

In the state of nature, this country was almost wholly covered with trees, many of which are of great magnitude. More than one hundred species are found, and the timber is of various qualities, affording to the farmer, ship-builder, carpenter, cooper, and cabinet-maker great opportunities of selecting what is most suitable for their different purposes. Of the oak only, there are fourteen or fifteen species, of which the over cup, *(Quercus macrocarpa)* affords the best timber. The post oak, *(Quercus obtusiloba)* is also much esteemed for the durability of its timber when put into the ground. The black locust, *(Robinia pseud-acacia)* and the honey locust, *(Gleditsia triacanthos)* are excellent for the ship-builders, and are much esteemed by them, particularly for the making of tree-nails. For furniture, they chiefly use the wild cherry, *(Prunas Virgiana)* and black walnut, *(Juglans nigra)* the former is little inferior to mahogany in beauty.

Nothing so much surprises the European on his first entrance into the western country, as the grandeur and beauty of many of these trees, and more particularly if he happens to arrive in the Spring, not less than ten species produce a profusion of beautiful blossoms, and the underwood consists mostly of some of our finest flowering shrubs. The trees comprise five species of Magnolia, with *Liriodendron tulipifera*, or tulip tree, *Robinia pseudacacia*, or black locust, *Guilandina dioica*, or coffee nut, and two species of horse chesnut, *Æsculus pavia* and *flava*. Amongst the shrubs are found the *Rhododendrons*, *Kalmias*, and *Azaleas*, with *Cercis Canadensis*, and *Cornus florida*.

The wild animals have mostly disappeared from the vicinity of the inhabited parts; none now remain that are dangerous, and but few that are destructive. The wolves sometimes take a sheep, or a small pig, but they are already becoming scarce, and will soon disappear. The squirrels are the greatest enemies the farmers have now to contend with, but are prevented from an inordinate increase by the frequency of *squirrel hunts* by the riflemen, which is encouraged by the land-holders.*

The price of land is so much varied by quality and situation, that no certain data can be given. Near the large towns, land is as high as near the cities in the eastern states, and in the most populous towns, the lots sell at a very high price. In February, 1816, land in the town of Louisville

* The squirrels have greatly increased since the country has become peopled by the whites, owing to the greater quantity of food afforded, by the opportunities they have of robbing the corn and wheat fields ; but the farmers occasionally give what they call " *a barbique*" in the woods, to the young riflemen, on the condition that they make a match at squirrel hunting, of six, eight, or ten, against a similar number, who also make a wager amongst themselves. The hog is killed, dressed, and roasted after the Indian method; this consists in digging a hole, the bottom of which they cover with hot stones ; on these the hog is laid, and covered over also with heated stones. There is plenty of liquor, and the *frolick* ends in shooting at a mark. I have heard of more than 2,000 squirrels being killed at one of these hunts, all with ball. Perhaps this circumstance contributes to render these people such skilful marksmen ; and as every man is necessitated to appropriate a portion of his land to timber for fuel and fences, the squirrels having refuge there, it will long continue to do so. Another enemy they keep within bounds, perhaps without designing it. Before the peaches are naturally mature, great quantities fall from the trees, apparently ripe ; to consume these, they turn the hogs into their orchards. On examining these peaches, in each may be found a small worm, of course produced by a winged insect, probably a *Cy-*

sold at the rate of 30,000 dollars per acre. The lands belonging to the United States government are sold at one uniform price, viz. two dollars per acre, with five years to pay it in, or one dollar, sixty-four cents cash. There are but few European families, who have been accustomed to sedentary employments, that could submit to the fatigues incident on clearing a forest, and converting it into arable land. To such, a resource is always open, as opportunisies are never wanting to purchase from the *Backwoodsman* what he calls *his improvement.* He is alarmed at the approach of population, and is anxious to remove farther back into the woods. The improvement consists in a log house, a peach, and perhaps an apple orchard, together with from ten, to thirty or forty acres of land, inclosed, and partially cleared. For this, seldom more than from fifty to a hundred dollars is asked, exclusive of the value of the land, which in most cases belongs to the United States, and may be purchased at the land office on the usual

---

nips. Those who are acquainted with the amazing powers of reproduction vested in insects, need not to be informed of the consequences if these were all suffered to arrive at maturity. Some of the farmers consider the woodpecker as an enemy, on account of the great number of perforations it makes in their apple trees, but as its food is insects, the same reasoning will apply as in the case above, and I think it to them an invaluable friend.

terms. Besides the land belonging to the United States, there are large tracts in the hands of speculators, from whom it may sometimes be purchased upon as good terms as from the government, and as liberal in point of credit; but in this case, care should be taken to examine if the title is good. Many of the speculators are anxious to sell, as the land-tax, although comparatively light, becomes heavy on very extensive purchases: it amounts to one dollar, twenty cents, per annum, on 100 acres of first-rate land; one dollar on 100 acres of second-rate; and sixty cents on third-rate. These sums are nearly in the proportion of $\frac{14}{20}$ of a penny per acre for first-rate; one halfpenny per acre for second-rate; and $\frac{7}{10}$ of a halfpenny per acre for third-rate. Some districts of upland may be purchased of the speculators at half a dollar, or 2s. 3d. per acre: this would answer well for sheep. No land tax is expected until five years after the purchase, when land becomes liable. They have two modes of clearing land; one by cutting the trees round, so as to kill them, and afterwards clearing away the underwood, the quantity of which is very small: this mode is called *girdling*, and is only resorted to by those who, to use their own phrase, are " *weak-handed*." The other mode is by cutting down the trees, dragging them into heaps, and burning them. This operation is almost always the subject of what they term a *frolic*, or in some places, a *bee*. It is necessary to remark, that in the early part of the settlement of a country like this, a great number of things occur necessary to be done, which require the united strength of numbers to effect. In those parts, money cannot purchase for the new settlers the required aid; but that kind and generous feeling which men have for each other, who are not rendered callous by the possession of wealth, or the dread of poverty, comes to his relief: his neighbours, even unsolicited, appoint a day when as a *frolic*, they shall, for instance, build him a house. On the morning of the appointed day they assemble, and divide themselves into parties, to each of which is assigned its respective duty; one party cuts down the trees, another lops and cuts them to proper lengths, a third is furnished with horses and oxen, and drags them to the spot designed for the scite of the house: another party is employed in making *shingles* to cover the roof, and at night all the materials are ready upon the spot; and on the night of the next day, he and his family sleep in their new habitation. No remuneration is expected, nor would it be received. It is considered the performance of a duty, and only lays him under the obligation to discharge the debt by doing the same to subsequent settlers. But this combination of labour in numbers, for the benefit of one individual, is not confined to the new comer only, it occurs frequently in the course of a year among the *old set-tlers*, with whom it is a continued bond of amity and social intercourse, and in no part of the world is *good neighbourship* found in greater perfection than in the western territory, or in America generally.

As the climate has already been spoken of, I shall only observe, that here, as in Upper Louisiana, the shortness and mildness of the winter is of immense advantage to the farmer. In parts where the winter is five or six months long, a great portion of time must necessarily be employed in providing food for the cattle during that season. Here very little time or land is necessary to be devoted to that purpose. The greatest part of the farmers scatter the seeds of pumpkins in the fields when planting the corn: no farther care is required, except throwing the pumpkins into the waggon when ripe. These, with the tops of the Indian corn, cut off when the ears are formed, give sufficient food for all the stock during winter. The pumpkins are raised with so little trouble, that they sell for a dollar per waggon load, and generally weigh from thirty to fifty pounds each, although some have been raised to exceed 200 pounds. Cattle and hogs eat them with avidity.

The vine flourishes in this region, and the

wheat can scarcely be surpassed, either for quality or abundance. With the exception of beans, *(Vicia faba)* and cauliflower, the culinary vegetables of Europe are raised in as much perfection as in England. In addition to these, they cultivate in their fields, amongst other crops, water-melons, musk-melons, squashes, and sweet potatoes, *(Convolvulus batatus.)* Cucumbers and beans, *(Phaseolus)* grow in much greater perfection than in England. The fruits are excellent, and in great abundance, particularly peaches and apples.

Very little of the agricultural labour falls on the women, who employ themselves in their domestic manufactures, in which they are both expert and industrious. Almost all grow some flax, and south of latitude 39°, they have what they call a *cotton patch.** Few are without sheep. By these means, the women are furnished with three staple articles, out of which they spin sufficient to produce almost all the clothing and other articles necessary for a family. Some have looms, and weave it themselves; others employ weavers, who follow that business as an occupation.†

---

* Cotton does not become an object of culture as a crop north of 36°.

† The manufacture of their woollens is much facilitated by

In the towns, many of the trades or manufactories are already established, that are calculated to furnish articles of the first degree of necessity; and some of those which produce articles necessary in a more advanced state of refinement. Amongst the first, are masons, stone-cutters, brickmakers, smiths, carpenters, wheelwrights, cabinetmakers, saddlers, boot and shoe makers, ship and boat builders, nailors, coppersmiths and brassfounders, wire-drawers and wire-makers, screw and hinge makers, gunsmiths, cutlers, machine makers, clock and watch makers, curriers, glovers, distillers, butchers, bakers, brewers, stocking makers, rope makers, coffee-mill makers, and a great number of others. There are also glass manufactories, cotton and woollen manufactories, iron foundries, potteries, floor-cloth manufactories, steam engine makers, glass cutting, silversmiths, looking-glass makers, printers, bookbinders, &c. &c. There is no part of the world where labour finds a better market than in the western country; this results from a state of things that will not admit of a speedy change. A very moderate sum of money enables a man to procure one or two hundred acres of land; the savings of

---

the establishment of carding machines: almost generally throughout the United States, some proprietors have two or three machines.

two or three years will enable a working man to effect this, if he is prudent; and although he can only cultivate a small part of it, and perhaps for the first two or three years, not more than will maintain his family, yet the accumulation of property by the regular and rapid advance in the value of his land, forms more than an equivalent to the savings of the labourer or mechanic. From this cause, there is a continued tendency in the labourers to turn to farming, as soon as they have acquired a little property: they are well aware that, by undertaking to bring *wild land* into a state of cultivation, they must undergo some hardships, and suffer some privations, but the state of ease, security, and independence which will assuredly follow, makes ample amends.

That produce of every kind, of the nature of provisions, will for a very long time remain low, may be presumed by attending to the following circumstances: first, the distance from a foreign market, causing a great expense in exportation: secondly, the great predominance of scattered population employed in farming, over that which is condensed in towns, or otherwise employed: and thirdly, the vast extent of land remaining west of the Alleghanies yet unoccupied; this will appear from the following statement of the area and population, in which all that part attached to the

u

Atlantic States is excluded. The population is taken as it stood in the census of 1810, since when, although there has been a great increase, yet it makes no very sensible difference when the extent of the country is considered.

	Area in square miles.	Population.
Ohio State,	43,860	230,760
Indiana State,	39,000	24,520
Illinois Territory,	52,000	12,282
Michigan Territory,	34,820	4,762
North West Territory,	106,830	1,000
Kentucky State,	40,110	406,511
Tenessee State,	43,200	261,727
Mississippi Territory,	88,680	40,352
Missouri Territory,	985,250	20,845
	1,433,750	1,002,759

By this statement, it appears that in 1810, there was only one inhabitant in near $1\frac{1}{2}$ square miles, or, (as there are 640 acres to the square mile) one inhabitant in every 900 acres, not one-tenth of these are residents in towns, nor one-fifth having any employment but agriculture.

The average population in England and Wales is 192 to the square mile. In Lancashire there are 400 inhabitants to the square mile, which allows but little more than an acre and a half to each individual.

Wages in the Western Country, to a labourer or husbandman, are about fifteen dollars, or £3 7s. 6d. per month, and his board, washing, &c. Carpenters, masons, and other handicraft men, average about one dollar and twenty-five cents per day, equal to 5s. 7½d. or one dollar and board. Shoemakers have about 4s. sterling for making a pair of shoes, and for a pair of boots about 11s. In the present state of things, flour, and other produce that is transferable to a foreign market, is higher than usual, but when not affected by a scarcity in Europe, will fall to the usual price, which is pretty near the following statement.

	American Money.			Eng. Money.	
	Dols.	Cents.		Shils.	Pence.
Flour, *per barrel*, ...	4	0	or	18	0
Indian corn meal, *per* 100*lbs*,....	0	40	—	1	9½
Potatoes, *per bushel*, ...	0	31	—	1	4½
Beef, mutton, and veal, *per lb*...	0	5	—	0	2½
Pork, *per do.*	0	4	—	0	2
Bacon, *per do.*.................	0	8	—	0	4½
Venison, *per do.*	0	4	—	0	2
Fowls, *each*	0	12½	—	0	7
Ducks, *do.*	0	25	—	1	1½
Geese, *do.*	0	62½	—	2	10
Turkies, *do.*	0	75	—	3	4½
Cheese, *per lb*.................	0	10	—	0	5¼
Butter, *per do.*.................	0	14	—	0	7¼
Cider, *per barrel*, ...	3	0	—	13	6
Whiskey, *per gallon*, ...	0	40	—	1	9½
Peach brandy, *per do*..........	0	80	—	3	7
Maple sugar, *per lb.*	0	10	—	0	5¼

By a comparison of this table with the rate of wages, it will appear that an industrious working man may support a family with great ease in this country.

Mellish, in his description of these parts, gives a statement of the prices of provisions and labour, which he closes by the following observations. " From this list of prices, taken in connexion with the value of labour, it will be seen, that an ordinary workman can procure for a day's work, fifty pounds of flour,—or twenty pounds of beef.—or three bushels of potatoes,—or twenty-seven pounds of pork,—or eight fowls,—or four ducks,—or two ordinary geese,—or one very large turkey."

The constitution of the state of Ohio declares that

1. All men are born equally free and independent.

2. All men have a natural right to worship God according to the dictates of their own conscience.

3. Trial by jury shall be inviolate.

4. Printing-presses shall be free.

5. Unwarrantable searches shall not be permitted.

6. Unnecessary rigor shall not be exercised.

7. Excessive bail shall not be required in bailable offences.

8. All penalties shall be proportioned to the nature of the offence.

9. The liberty of the people to assemble together, to consult for the public good, and to bear arms in their own defence, is guaranteed.

10. Hereditary emoluments, honours, and priveleges are forever prohibited.

11. Slavery is forever prohibited, and it is declared that " No indenture of any negro or mulatto, hereafter made and executed out of the state, or if made in the state, where the term of service exceeds one year, shall be of the least validity, except those given in the case of apprenticeship."

12. " Religion, morality, and knowledge being essentially necessary to the good government and happiness of mankind, schools, and the means of instruction, shall be forever encouraged by legis-

lative provision, not inconsistent with the rights of conscience."

The government is legislative and executive, and regulates the judicial and military authority.

The legislature consists of a senate and house of representatives. The senators are elected *bienni-ally*, the representatives *annually*, by the people, and one half vacate their seats every year. Every free white male, who is a citizen of the United States, and has resided in that state one year, has a vote for a representative; if he has resided two years, he can vote for a senator.

Every citizen qualified to vote for a representative, and above twenty-five years of age, is also eligible to be himself elected: if above thirty years of age, he is eligible to become a senator.

The governor is also chosen by the people, and serves for two years: he cannot by law be elected more than three times in succession.

The election is carried on throughout the state on the same day, and during the same hours, viz. from ten to four o'clock. There is a poll in every township, and it is conducted by ballot; each elector hands in a slip of paper, containing the name of the candidate for whom he gives his vote, at which time his own name is registered. By this means, the whole business of election is begun and terminated in one day, without any noise or disturbance.

The justices are appointed by the people of their respective townships, and retain their office only three years, unless re-elected.

In the military of the state, the captains and the subaltern officers are chosen by those in their respective company districts, who are subject to military duty.

Majors are elected by captains and subalterns.

Colonels are elected by majors, captains, and subalterns.

Brigadier-generals are elected by the commissioned officers of their respective brigades.

Major-generals and quarter-master-generals are appointed by joint ballot of both houses of the legislature.

The governor is commander-in-chief, and appoints the adjutants.

In regard to the manners of the people west of the Alleghanies, it would be absurd to expect that a general character could be now formed, or that it will be for many years yet to come. The population is at present compounded of a great number of nations, not yet amalgamated, consisting of emigrants from every state in the Union, mixed with English, Irish, Scotch, Dutch, Swiss, Germans, French, and almost from every country in Europe. In some traits they partake in common with the inhabitants of the Atlantic States, which results from the nature of their government. That species of hauteur which one class of society in some countries show in their intercourse with the other, is here utterly unknown. By their constitution, the existence of a privileged order, vested by birth with hereditary privileges, honours, or emoluments, is for ever interdicted. If, therefore, we should here expect to find that contemptuous feeling in man for man, we should naturally examine amongst those clothed with judicial or military authority; but we should search in vain. The justice on the bench, or the officer in the field, is respected and obeyed whilst discharging the functions of his office, as the representative or agent of the law, enacted for the *good of all;* but should he be tempted to treat even the least wealthy of his neighbours or fellow-citizens with contumely, he would soon find that he could not do it with impunity. Travellers from Europe, in passing through the western country, or indeed any part of the United States, ought to be previously acquainted with this part of the American character, and more particularly if they have been in the habit of treating with contempt, or irritating with abuse, those whom accidental circumstances may have placed in a situation to administer to their wants. Let no one here indulge himself in abusing the waiter or hostler at an inn :. that waiter or hostler is probably a citizen, and does not, nor cannot conceive, that a situation in which he discharges a duty to society, not in itself dishonourable, should subject him to insult : but this feeling, so far as I have experienced, is entirely defensive. I have travelled near 10,000 miles in the United States, and never met with the least incivility or affront.

The Americans in general are accused by travellers of being inquisitive. If this be a crime, the western people are guilty; but for my part I must say that it is a practice that I never was disposed to complain of, because I always found them as ready to answer a question as to ask one, and therefore I always came off a gainer by this kind of barter; and if any traveller does not, it is his own fault. As this leads me to notice their general conduct to strangers, I feel myself bound by gratitude and regard to truth, to speak of their hospitality. In my travels through the inhabited parts of the United States, not less than 2000 miles was through parts where there were no taverns, and where a traveller is under the necessity of appealing to the hospitality of the inhabitants. In no one instance has my appeal been fruitless, although in many cases the furnishing of a bed has been evidently attended with inconvenience, and in a great many instances no remuneration would be received. Other European travellers have experienced this liberal spirit of hospitality, and some have repaid it by calumny. These calumnies have reached them: they are well acquainted with what Weld and a person who calls himself Ashe have said of them.* In respect to their moral character, my experience reaches chief-

---

* As the book published by this Ashe contains numberless statements, bearing in themselves such evidences of being void of truth as to deprive him of all claim to veracity, and as it has already sunk into the oblivion it merits, the malignant falsehoods propagated by him, respecting America and the American people, should have remained unnoticed by me, had I not witnessed the just indignation it has excited in that country, and also found that Ashe had been received and treated with the greatest kindness by the very people whom he has so grossly libelled. His statements are too numerous, and many of them too absurd, to deserve a serious refutation; but I think it a duty due both to myself and to my country to state, that his description of the American people, and the accusations he makes against them, are void of foundation. If Mr. Ashe saw any instance to warrant his observations, he must have kept the worst of company.

ly to the western, middle, and some of the southern states. In the western states, I noticed that very few of the houses in which I slept had either locks or bolts on the doors, and that the jails were in general without a single tenant.

It has already been observed that no people discharge the social duties, as respects the character of neighbours, better, and I believe no country, having a population equal to the United States, can exhibit the records of their courts containing fewer statements of crimes committed against the laws.

The more northerly parts of the states of Ohio and Indiana, together with the whole of the Illinois and western territories, including an area of about 128,130,000 acres, comprehends that part which, in the beginning of this article, has been noticed as possessing a different character in its natural state. The original state of the region already spoken of was that of a continued forest, not convertible into a state fit for cultivation without great pains and labour. This region is an assemblage of woodland and prairie or savannas intermixed; the portions of each varying in extent, but the aggregate area of the prairies exceeding that of the woodland in the proportion of three or four to one. The soil of this part is inferior to none in North

America, or perhaps in the world. In a state of nature, these prairies are covered with a luxuriant growth of grass and herbaceous plants, affording a most abundant supply of food for the stock of the new settler; and it is worthy of notice, that any part of these prairies, when constantly fed on by cattle, becomes covered with white clover and the much esteemed blue grass, *(Poa compressa)* as frequent pasturing seems to give those plants a predominance over all others.

In the geological formation, this country also differs in some degree from the one entirely covered with wood in its natural state. The surface is much more level, and the strata more regular and undisturbed. In general the order of the strata is sand lying on sand-stone, afterwards lime-stone, beneath which is argillaceous schist lying on coal. For the settler who is not habitually accustomed to the felling of trees, and who has the courage to fix himself on wild land, this is by much the best part of the United States, excepting Upper Louisiana. If he places his house at the edge of one of these prairies, it furnishes him food for any number of cattle he may choose to keep. The woodland affords him the materials necessary for his house, his fire, and fences, and with a single yoke of oxen, he can in general immediately reduce any part of his prairie land to a state of tillage. Had this portion of the country been placed at no greater distance from the Alleghanies than the woody region, it would undoubtedly have been the first settled; but being situated from 500 to 1000 miles beyond those mountains, and separated from them by one of the most fertile countries in the world, the consequence is, that emigrants are so well satisfied with what advantages a first view of the country presents, that they are anxious to sit down as soon as possible. Another reason why this portion of the wild lands has not been more rapidly settled, is the total indifference of the American farmer to the present or future value of coal. This arises in part from his prejudice against the use of it for fuel, but more from his want of knowledge of its vast importance to other countries, and a consequent want of foresight. The farmer who is possessed of 500 acres of land, expects that in time it will probably be divided into ten properties or farms by his posterity, each of which must be supplied with timber for fuel and fences: he wishes, therefore, that the land unreclaimed may remain covered with timber, as a reserve for posterity, although perhaps he has an excellent bed of coal at no great distance beneath the surface.

Nothing so strongly indicates the superiority of the western country, as the vast emigrations to it from the eastern and southern states. In passing through the upper parts of Virginia, I observed a great number of farms that had been abandoned, on many of which good houses had been erected, and fine apple and peach orchards had been planted. On enquiring the reason, I was always informed that the owners had gone to the western country. From the New England states the emigrations are still more numerous. They mostly cross the Hudson river betwixt Albany and Newburg, and must pass through Cayuga in their way to Pittsburg. I was informed by an inhabitant of Cayuga, in April 1816, that more than 15,000 waggons had passed over the bridge at that place within the last eighteen months, containing emigrants to the western country.

In making the following remarks, and in giving such instructions and information as will be useful to those who purpose to emigrate to America, I disclaim any wish to promote emigration. Much distress has arisen to emigrants, either from having entertained false conceptions, or from a want of knowledge how to conduct themselves after their arrival in the United States. I have witnessed that distress, and traced it to the cause : my wish is to obviate it.

The remarks that follow will only apply to such as the law permits to expatriate themselves, and of course the present state or future prospects of manufactures in the United States will form no part of the subjects to be considered. But the inutility of the law, prohibiting the emigration of manufacturers or machinists to the United States, is so obvious to any one acquainted with the interior of that country, that they are at a loss to conceive why it continues to exist. It is still more surprising that it should yet be enforced in a country where excess of population is a subject of complaint, where means have been devised to check the rapidity of its progress, and where the classes denied the privilege of expatriation are complained of as being an incumbrance, and are daily adding more and more to the distress of the nation, in the picture of which they stand the most prominent figure. Whoever is intimately acquainted with the interior of the United States, knows that cotton and woollen manufactories are spread throughout the union, and that they have found their way even to the west of the Alleghanies. At Nashville, in Tennessee; Lexington, in Kentucky; at Cincinnati, Beaver, and at Pittsburg, and many other places, there are large cotton and woollen establishments.

In the eastern and middle states there are many hundreds of factories, abundantly supplied with managers and machine-makers from Britain, of

which there is such a redundancy, that a very considerable number have resorted to agriculture.
Whether manufactories will succeed in America,
or to what degree, time alone can determine; but
that their progress can be in the least impeded by
restrictive laws, prohibiting the emigration of manufacturers or machinists from this country, is now
absolutely impossible.

The first step that an emigrant ought to take,
should be to provide himself with a proper certificate, setting forth his trade or profession, and testifying that he has never been employed in manufactures, or machine making, or in works of brass,
iron, or steel, appertaining to manufactures. This
certificate must be signed by the minister and
churchwardens of the parish to which he belongs;
and if also by a magistrate, it will render it of
more effect.

Most articles of furniture being cheaper in the
United States than in Britain, nothing of that
kind ought to be taken, as they would, in all probability, suffer damage. Feather beds and bedding,
on the contrary, should be preserved; and for
packing clothes, &c. trunks are preferable to heavy
and clumsy boxes. On arriving at the port from
whence the emigrant expects to sail, his first care
should be to ascertain if his certificate is sufficient,

which he may be acquainted with at the custom-house; and he must be careful not to pay for his passage until he be well assured that he shall be permitted to proceed.

The port in the United States to which it will be the interest of the emigrant to sail, will depend on his views or his prospects. A wide field is open to him, and he ought to make himself acquainted with its geography before he decide on this point.

For a very great portion of emigrants, the countries west of the Alleghanies, say Ohio, Indiana, Kentucky, Tennessee, or the Illinois, offer by much the best prospects; and to get to those countries, Philadelphia or Baltimore are the best ports. If the intention be to proceed to the lower part of the Ohio, Baltimore is preferable to Philadelphia, and the best way will be to go from thence to Wheeling, on the Ohio, ninety-five miles below Pittsburg, and the road is much less difficult. The port to which the emigrant will sail being determined, the next consideration is sea store; and he will do well to recollect that most probably both himself and his family will be sea sick for some days, and that, during its continuance, if he is a steerage passenger, both he and his wife will have an utter aversion to the trouble of cooking: he must therefore pro-

vide some cold meat to last during that time : either
fowls or veal would be the best. For the general
sea store it would be difficult to prescribe rules.
The quantity will of course depend on the number
to be provided for, and the quality, on their taste,
and in some measure on the season of the year. If
there are small children, some oatmeal and some
molasses will be found very useful and wholesome,
as it will furnish a food much more conducive to
their health than salt provisions. For the general
sea store, tea, coffee, sugar, biscuits, butter, cheese,
a few hams, salt, soap, candles, &c. will be necessary. Sufficient should be laid in to last at least
eight weeks, in particular for Baltimore, as sometimes vessels are a week or ten days in going up
the Chesapeake after passing the Capes. A due
regard to cleanliness during the voyage is recommended ; to admit as much air between decks as
the weather will permit, and to take a few bottles
of vinegar to sprinkle on the floor occasionally; and
if it can be practised, fumigation, by putting a red
hot piece of iron in a kettle of pitch, will be found
salutary. On arriving at the desired port, if the
emigrant has any letters of introduction, he should
deliver them immediately : his friends may probably assist him in finding a proper place where
his family may rest a few days after the fatigues of
the voyage. His next care will be to land his
trunks, bedding, &c. and get them deposited in a

place of safety. If he have not a letter of introduction to any one in the city where he first lands, he ought to be on his guard. In every one of the maritime cities in America, a great number of small stores are established for the sale of spirituous liquors, &c. Many of these are kept by natives of Great Britain, and some of those who keep them are so devoid of principle as to induce emigrants to remain in the cities, under various pretences, but chiefly holding out a prospect of employment, when their real purpose is to tempt them to spend their money with them.

So many emigrants arrive at all the principal ports in the United States, that there is very little chance of employment, and almost the whole of the distress that has been reported to exist in America, has arisen from the number of emigrants who have foolishly lingered in the cities until they have spent all their money.

It shall be supposed that the design of the emigrant is to proceed to the countries east of the Alleghanies, in which case, he ought not to stay more than two or three days in the city. When he first lands, he will find that great numbers of waggons start from Philadelphia to Pittsburg, or from Baltimore to Pittsburg or Wheeling, every day. The charge is by the hundred weight, both

for passengers and their luggage, and the rate is
variable from five to seven dollars per hundred;
but the men may go cheaper if they chuse to walk
over the mountains, which is recommended. The
waggoners travel with great economy: many
of them carry a small camp-kettle with them, in
which they cook their provisions, and some have
even a bed in their waggons, in which they sleep
at night. A traveller who chooses to adopt a similar mode, may travel very cheap; or as there
are plenty of inns on the roads, he can be ac-
commodated every night with beds, at a very
reasonable rate. When the emigrant arrives at
Pittsburg or Wheeling, he will find that numbers
of Europeans and Americans are arriving there
every day, and the same causes that operated
against them in the maritime cities, as respects
employment, will, in some degree, have an effect
here; but as he will have occasion for information,
it would be advisable for him to stop a few days, to
make enquiries. If he find it necessary to descend the Ohio, the best mode of proceeding will
be to enquire for one or more families, who have
intentions of going to the same neighbourhood as
himself, who may join him in the purchase of an *ark*,
one of the kind of vessels in which families descend.
These arks are built for sale, for the accommodation of families descending the river, and for the
conveyance of produce. They are flat-bottomed,

and square at the ends, and are all made of the same dimensions, being fifty feet in length, and fourteen in breadth; which last is limited, because it often happens that they must pass over the falls at Louisville, when the river is at a low state, at which time they pass betwixt two rocks in the *Indian schute*, only fifteen feet asunder.* These arks are covered, and are managed by a steering oar, which can be lifted out of the water. The usual price is seventy-five dollars for each, which will accommodate three or four families, as they carry from twenty-five to thirty tons; and it frequently happens that the ark can be sold for nearly what it cost, six or eight hundred miles lower down the river.

After the arrival of the emigrant on the Ohio, the next step he takes is a very important one :— much depends on his movement, and it is at that point when he has the greatest need of counsel and advice. From Europe until he arrives on the Ohio, general rules may apply, but now his future destination depends on his choice, and no general rule can be given to direct that choice, because emigrants are of so many different descriptions.

---

* There are regular pilots resident at Louisville, who conduct the boats over the falls, and deliver them safe at Shipping Port :—they charge two dollars for pilotage.

In order that these remarks may have a general application, the emigrants shall be considered as consisting of several classes, the remarks shall be applied to each class separately, and terminate with some general observations.

The first class of emigrants may be composed of labourers, who have no other trade or profession, and from whose services, more is expected to result from bodily strength, than from ingenuity or education. If a man of this class will work, he has nothing to fear in the interior of America :—he possesses all the requisites for a farmer, excepting skill, and that he may soon obtain. A great number of farmers have more land inclosed in fence than they can well manage : ask one of these the reason, he replies, " I want help." An assistant enables him to cultivate a portion of his land that would otherwise become overrun with weeds. The emigrant cannot expect full wages in the commencement, but if he be attentive, he may in one year become so expert as to be entitled to what is usually paid to husbandmen, from twelve to fifteen dollars per month, and board.

But when employment is obtained, the most difficult thing remains yet to be done. The man he lives with, and for whom he works, most probably makes his own cider, a portion of which is distilled into brandy: both these articles are kept, in considerable quantities, in the farmer's house. The emigrant is liberally supplied with them, and can obtain them at a cheap rate elsewhere; but he must avoid indulging too much, particularly in the spirits. He is not accustomed to a profusion of this article, and may, by too frequent use, acquire a habit, that will ruin all his future prospects in life. If his conduct is proper, he may associate with the sons of the neighbouring farmers, many of whom know that their ancestors became proprietors of land from a beginning not more promising than his: even his employer was probably the helper to some one formerly. Before this man can become a complete American farmer, he must learn a number of things, not connected with agriculture in some other countries. He must learn to handle the axe dexterously, as he will often be employed to cut down trees. He must also learn, not only to distinguish the different species of trees, but also to know by their appearance whether they will suit the purpose for which they are wanted.

The second class of emigrants to be considered, are those who have trades or professions, and yet are too poor to enter into business for themselves. The primary object of a person of this description is, of course, employment: the commodity he has to dispose of is *labour*, for which he wants a market. So much of this is daily brought into the sea-ports by the arrival of emigrants, that they are always over-stocked; he must look for a better chance:—this chance the country will afford him. If his trade or profession be such as is followed in a city, he may remain two days before he goes to the country; if unsuccessful in his enquiries for work, he ought not to remain longer. During his stay, he ought to enquire amongst those in his own profession, where he may hope to obtain employment; it is very likely they may furnish references which will be very useful to him. In travelling, this man ought not to be sparing in his enquiries; he is not in the least danger of receiving a rude or an uncivil answer, even if he should address himself to a *squire*, (so justices are called.) It is expected in America, that every man shall attend to his own concerns; and if a man who is out of work ask for employment, it is considered as a very natural thing.

He ought to make his situation and profession known at the taverns where he stops, and rather to court than to shun conversation with any that he may find assembled there. He will seldom or never meet with a repulse, as it gives them an opportunity of making enquiries respecting the " *old country*," (the term usually applied to the British Islands.)

Should he fail in procuring employment at his own business, he has all the advantages of the first man, in agriculture. The countries west of the Alleghany Mountains afford the greatest advantages of any part of the United States, to emigrants of this or the preceding description; and when they arrive at the head of the Ohio, the facility of descending that river opens to them a vast field, in which labour must, for ages to come, find a good market, as the vast tract of fine land yet unsettled will induce such an avidity for farming, that labourers, or men who have trades or professions, will adopt that line of life whenever they can raise the means of purchasing land. For this reason a very long time must elapse before there can be such a redundancy of labour as to reduce its value. Some of the trades that are carried on in the large towns are enumerated at page 296.

The man possessed of some property, say from 200 to 1000 pounds, has more need of cautionary advice than either of the former. But no knowledge can be conveyed to him, that will be so valuable as what results from his own experience and observation. He is advised to deposit his money in a bank, or vest it in government stock immediately on landing. His next object is to determine in what line of life he shall employ himself and his capital. In this he should avoid being too hasty. If it is known that he has money, he will probably be tempted to enter into speculations, both by his own countrymen and others. Designing men are much more likely to hold out such temptations than men with honest and honourable intentions; and until he has acquired a competent knowledge of men and things, it is dangerous for him to embark in business. It should have been premised, that he ought, if possible, to take with him letters of introduction to some persons in the United States, experienced in matters of business, whom he might occasionally consult. If he decide on mercantile business, or keeping a store, he ought by all means to procure a situation in a merchant's counting-house or in a store for one year at least: even if with only trifling wages, he will still be a gainer. If he adopt agriculture, he ought to obtain, if possible, an assistant who knows the management of crops, and the mode of working the ground: such a person will be necessary, at least for two years. If he should not succeed in procuring such a man, he must keep on good terms with his neighbours, who will cheerfully tell him what is necessary to be done. In purchasing his land, he ought not to depend entirely on his own judgment, unless he has made an extensive tour through the country, and attentively considered the subject of land. He will find some remarks applicable to that subject amongst those addressed to a farmer.

In a great many trades or professions, the emigrant who has a capital and a trade or profession, may meet with less difficulty than any of the preceding, if he act with caution. Much in this case depends on making a judicious choice in determining where to establish his business. In most trades, the country beyond the Alleghany Mountains, say Ohio, Kentucky, or Tennessee, hold out greater advantages than the rest of the Union, the profits in business being greater, and the expence of living much less: the climate also is more suitable to European constitutions, as the extreme betwixt the heat of summer and cold of winter is much less than in the Atlantic States. In some trades he may be expected to keep journeymen, perhaps Americans, from whom he is advised not to exact that servility of deportment expected from subordinates in other countries. He may be faithfully served without it. He loses nothing by this, as those who are his employers or customers will make no such exactions from him.

There are several objects in America that present themselves to the capitalist, in which he may vest his property with perfect security, and if he act

judiciously, he will have no reason to complain of
his profits. The most prominent object that offers
itself is land. Of this, immense tracts may always
be had, and in particular from the government of
the United States. The price is two dollars per
acre; one-fourth of the money to be paid down,
the rest by instalments in five years. The degree
of advantage to be derived from land purchases,
depends in a great measure on the judgment and
foresight of the speculator, to whom the country
west of the Alleghanies offers the best field. A
very great majority of the emigrants to that part
have only farming in view, and the establishment
of towns does not keep pace with the increase of
interspersed population. There are a great many
places, which, from the nature of things, must become the scites of towns: a person of judgment
and observation would easily point them out. The
formation of a number of proximate settlements has
an invariable tendency to raise the price of land in
their vicinity: for this reason a rich man, who
purchases a large tract of land on speculation, con-
sults his best interests by a liberal policy towards
those who first settle on his property. Let it be
supposed that he purchases four miles square; this
is sixteen square miles or sections, or 10,240 acres,
which for cash costs 16,896 dollars, or £3801 12s.
English money. On this property he ought to
possess a scite convenient for a village, and he

should also have a water-fall. If he lays the whole out in quarter sections, he will have sixty-four of 160 acres each. Let him lay out the village, and sell, in the first instance, only the intermediate subdivisions, at moderate terms and liberal credit: the reserved subdivisions, together with the village lots, will in a short time rise to a very great value. The next object of importance is coal, and although the investment of capital in that way may not so speedily produce profit as in land, yet it holds out great advantages. It has already been stated that coal is abundant in the western country, and that a considerable portion of that region is prairie: it has also been observed, that the existence of a bed of coal scarcely enhances the price of the land under which it lies. In most parts of the Atlantic States, fifty years ago, one acre of cleared land was worth five of woodland. Since that time innumerable towns and villages have been established, and the old cities and villages have increased. Every city or town may be considered as the centre of a circle, within the area of which one acre of woodland is now of much more value than the same extent of the finest meadow. These areas are continually increasing, and consequently the aggregate value of timber. At a period not very remote the larger cities must resort to the use of coal, and nothing is more certain than that a time will come when that article will be as valuable to America as it is now to England.

The emigrant who goes to America with the intention of applying himself to farming, should take with him some seed wheat of the best kinds, and if he can procure it, perhaps the Syrian wheat *(Triticum compositum)* might be worth a trial. It has a much better chance of answering in America than in England, and particularly south of 40 degrees of latitude; also a small quantity of lucerne, saintfoin, and vetches: either the seeds or the roots of the two former, but the roots would be preferable. It might also be adviseable to take a small bag of hay seeds from some of the best meadows. Farming implements can be had in any part of the United States, well adapted to the different purposes for which they are wanted. In determining a situation, he has the choice of any climate from latitude 29 to 44 degrees, comprehending the regions suitable for the culture of sugar, cotton, and grain. If his views are governed by the determination to adopt any particular culture, he will of course settle in the region suitable. If sugar, he will go south of $31\frac{1}{2}°$; if cotton, south of $36°$: for corn the most agreeable is from $36°$ to $41°$, as further north the severity and length of the winters render the climate less desirable. A farmer, on settling in America, ought not rashly to set up his opinions or former practices against those of the old settlers. Many things which may appear to him at first to be wrong or unnecessary, will be found, on farther experience, both right and expedient; but if he cultivates the good will of his neighbours, and follows their advice, he will not go wrong. He will soon find the succession of crops and the mode of culture vary much from what he has experienced in England, and that a differently modified climate, and a sun more nearly vertical, greatly change the order of the things to which he has been accustomed. He will find his rye harvest to commence in June, and that of his wheat soon after : the oats follow next, and afterwards, if he have a meadow, his grass will be ready for the scythe; then come his potatoes, and lastly his Indian corn. If the emigrant purchases and settles upon what is called wild land, one of his first cares ought to be to plant a peach and apple orchard, and he ought to plant the two sorts alternate, say one peach betwixt two apple trees, and not plant the apple trees less than thirty feet asunder. The peach tree soon comes to maturity, and is short lived : they will become of little value by the time the apple trees are in want of room. In the woody region, the axe is for some time the chief implement in the hands of the settler, and he feels a considerable degree of repugnance at the destruction of so much fine timber ; but this soon subsides. If he has the courage to proceed as far west as the Illinois, the North-west Territories, or to the west of the Mississippi, the prairies afford him the means of settling without much trouble.

In the early part of the settlement of the rich countries beyond the Alleghanies, agues were very prevalent, and it will perhaps be found, that all countries in a state of nature are liable to this disease in the proportion of their fertility, which has a tendency to produce it, from the vast quantity of vegetable matter which goes to decay in autumn. As this applies generally in those regions, the new settler has no means of avoiding the consequence but by precautions and preventives : but as it has also a local influence, he may, by a judicious choice of a situation, render himself and family less liable to its attacks. As the first settlers have the choice of the whole country, it is very natural that they should adopt the alluvion of the rivers, both on account of the superior fertility of the soil, and the facilities it gives to the transportation of produce ; and many in so doing sacrifice their health to their apparent interest. It must be admitted, that some of the valleys in which the rivers flow are as healthy as the uplands ; but this depends on whether the river overflows its banks or not, or on the existence or non-existence of stagnant water in the neighbourhood. As to precautions, the emigrant is apprized that in these countries the dews are very copious, and begin to fall even before sunset. Let him avoid as much as possible exposure either to this or rain ; or if unavoidably exposed, he must take off his wet clothes as soon as possible ; and if he has flannel shirts, in order to change after copious perspiration, he will find benefit in them. An important consideration in this respect is the quality of the water used in his family ; of course, the purer this is the better. The settler cannot be expected to be capable of analyzing it, but he may discover the presence of sulphur, iron, an acid, or an alkali, by tests always in his power to procure. Sulphur may be detected by laying a piece of bright silver in the water, which turns black if that substance is held in solution. A little of the inner bark of any of the oaks, infused in a glassful, turns the water black, if iron is present. Paper, stained blue by the petals of almost any flower of that colour being rubbed upon it, turns green by being dipped in water impregnated with alkali, or red if an acid.

The settler who is accustomed to malt liquor may, with very little trouble, brew his own ale. Barley is cultivated west of the Alleghanies, and hops grow wild in abundance :—the use of this beverage is supposed to be a preventive to the ague. Almost every family has a supposed cure for this complaint; and every one who visits or sees those affected has a favourite remedy, all differing from each other; but the physicians, in the Western Country, treat it with bark and laudanum : of these the emigrant ought to lay in a sufficiency to administer to his family in case of need.

It has already been observed, that the emigrants to this country are almost of every nation in Europe, but it is a remarkable and striking fact, that the Germans, Dutch, and Swiss succeed much better than those from any other country. This is not so much owing to greater industry or economy, as to the more judicious mode they adopt in settling. In general, before these people emigrate they form associations, lay down their plans, and send an agent over in whom they can confide. He purchases for them a suitable extent of land, and prepares the way: when their arrangements are made, they move over in one body. This system has always been followed by these people, and the consequences are visible in almost every part of the United States, but more particularly in the states of New York, New Jersey, and Pennsylvania, in all parts of which they are in possession of the best lands. The appearance of comfort, ease, and independence exhibited by one of these little colonies is so visible that the traveller who does not perceive it at first sight, must be very deficient in discernment. Some of the colonies of this kind, besides the tie of common interest, have another bond of union, which is a similarity of sentiment and belief in their religious opinions ; this, in some instances, has operated as a cause for regulating their system of colonization : but perhaps that which has most generally influenced them is the circumstance of their language not being the general language of the United States, an inconvenience much less felt by a colony than by an isolated family ; but let the cause be what it may, the effect is very manifest, and may be easily accounted for. In the early settlement of any particular district of *new country,** its progress in improvements is slow, until a grist and a saw mill are erected, after which the change is very rapid. Every planter in the vicinity, by the aid of the saw mill, is able to erect a handsome frame-house. The grist mill enables him to convert his wheat into flour fit for a market, and he boldly engages and employs hands to assist him in converting the forest into fields, yielding luxuriant crops. These two kinds of mills are the most necessary objects in a new colony ; but there are many others, such as roads, bridges, &c. all of which are much sooner effected by a colony having an union of interest, and of course an union of action.

---

* The term *new country* signifies one newly settled.

The rapidity with which one of these colonies acquires wealth or property will appear by a comparison of their present state with their situation when they first sat down ; and for the sake of example, one of those societies shall be selected, and a review taken of their progress. This is the Harmonist Society, situated about 20 miles from Pittsburg. They came from Wirtemburg in Germany, where finding themselves oppressed and persecuted by a church and state union, they determined to flee to a land where no human authority would dare to insult the Deity, by arrogating to itself the right of dictating how He shall be worshipped, and where they are too wise or too honest to suppose they can force belief. This country is America; and in the year 1803 they sent George Rapp and others, as deputies, who fixed on a situation about twenty miles from Pittsburg.

In 1804, the society embarked at Amsterdam in three ships, two of which arrived at Philadelphia, and the other at Baltimore. In the November of that year forty families removed with Mr. Rapp, and before winter they built nine log-houses. In the spring of 1805, they were followed by fifty more families, making in all ninety. The whole of their property was about 20,000 dollars : this they laid out in the purchase of 9000 acres of land, which, together with their mental and physical powers, in the spring of 1805 formed the whole of their possessions. In the summer of this year they built 46 log-houses, a large barn, a grist mill, and cleared 205 acres of land.

" In 1806, a large inn was built, partly of stone; a frame-barn, 100 feet long; a blue dyer's shop; an oil-mill : they also established a tannery. 358 acres of land were cleared.

" In 1807 they erected a number of buildings; amongst which was a saw-mill and a brewery ; 400 acres of land were cleared, and four acres of vines were planted.

" In 1808 they built a meeting-house of brick, together with dwelling-houses and stables, and a bridge over the Conaquenesing creek, 220 feet long. A considerable quantity of land was cleared.

" In the year 1809 they erected a fulling-mill, an oil-mill, a mill for breaking hemp, a grist mill, and a large brick warehouse, with a wine cellar beneath, arched over. The produce of this year was—4500 bushels of rye, 4500 bushels of wheat, 6000 bushels of Indian corn, 10,000 bushels of potatoes, 5000 bushels of oats, 4000 lbs. of flax and hemp, 100 bushels of barley brewed into beer, and 50 gallons of sweet oil from the white poppy.

" In 1810 they began the manufacture of *broad-cloth*, from the wool of their Merino sheep ; fixed up a carding machine, two spinning Jennies, and built a factory for twenty looms.

" In the year 1811 the property of the society was estimated as follows :—

	Dollars.
9000 acres of land, with improvements,..........	90,000
Stock of provisions for one year for 800 persons,..	25,000
Stock of goods, spirits, manufactures, leather, implements of husbandry, &c. &c.	50,000
Dwelling-houses, ...	18,000
Mills, machinery, and public buildings,..........	21,000
Horses, cattle, hogs, and poultry, ...	10,000
1000 sheep, one-third of them Merinoes, of which one ram cost 1000, ...	6,000
	220,000

The progress made by a small colony of Swiss, who settled in the Indiana Territory about the same time as the society at Harmony, is not less rapid. It consisted of eleven families, who united in forming a vineyard, from which, in 1811, they made more than 2000 gallons of wine.

CATALOGUE

OF SOME OF

THE MORE RARE OR VALUABLE PLANTS

Discovered in the Neighbourhood of St. Louis and on the Missouri.

Leersia Lenticularis, Woods, American Bottom, St. Louis.
Aristida Pallens, Hills on the Merrimac.
Stipa Juncea, Prairies, Aricaras to the Mandans.
—— *Membranacea,* Fort Mandan. *Probably not a Stipa.*
Aira Brevifolia, Great Prairie.
Festuca Spicata, common on the Missouri.
Cynosurus secundus, Mississippi bluffs.
Hordeum Jubatum, valleys near the Aricaras.
*Allionia Ovata, banks of the Missouri, above the Big Bend.
———— *Linearis,* ⎱ bluffs near the Aricara village.
———— *Hirsuta,* ⎰
Plantago Lagopus, Alluvion of the Missouri, common.
———— *Elongata,* near the Maha village.
Eleagnus Argentea, bluffs near the Mandan nation.
Hippophae Argentea, Mahas, Platte, Ottoes, Missouri.
Pulmonaria Sibirica, high up the Merrimac river.
———— *Lanceolata,* opposite the Aricara village.

---

* These three species of *Allionia* together with the two species of *Bartonia*, have the singular property of flowering in the night; they burst forth just at sun-set, and perish at its rising.

Batschia Canescens, prairie about St. Louis.

———— *Gmelini*, American Bottom, Illinois,

———— *Longiflora*, first occurs near the mouth of the **Platte,** on ascending the Missouri.

Onosmodium Molle, about St. Louis.

Dodecatheon Meadia, prairie behind St. Louis.

Phacelia Fimbriata, at Point L'Abbadie, on the Missouri, *with white flowers.*

Cynoglossum Glomeratum, Big Bend, Missouri.

Solanum Heterandrum, about the Aricara village.

Ribes Aureum, Little Cedar Island, Missouri.

Salsola Depressa, on the Missouri, near the mouth of Knife River.

Hydrocotyle Ambigua, rocks on the Mississippi, near Herculaneum.

Selinum acaule, on the alluvion of the Missouri, from the river Naduet to the Mahas.

Seseli Divaricatum, Missouri Bluffs, at the mouth of the L'eau qui court.

Linum Lewisii, on Cannon Ball river.

———— *Rigidum*, on the Missouri bluffs, common.

Yucca Angustifolia, Missouri bluffs, opposite the mouth of Papillon Creek.

Lilium Catesbæi, prairie about St. Louis.

———— *Umbellatum*, bluffs near the Mandan village.

Rumex Venosus, Big bend, Missouri.

Gaura Coccinea,
Oenothera Albicaulis, } bluffs Aricara village.

———— *Macrocarpa*, near St. Louis.

Eriogonum Pauciflorum, } near the Minetaree villages on the
———— *Sericeum,* } Missouri, both growing together.

Cactus Viviparus, Missouri bluffs, above the Poncar village.

Bartonia Ornata, }
———— *Nuda,* } on the bluffs above Knife River.

Geum Triflorum, head waters of Blackbird Creek.

Potentilla Arguta, bluffs above the Aricara village.

Ranunculus Multifidus, in stagnant pools near the Sepulchre bluffs.

Stachys Fœniculum, Missouri bluffs.

Capraria Multifida, American Bottom, Illinois.

Martynia Proboscidea, St. Louis.

Penstemon Erianthera, common on the bluffs from the Big Bend to the Aricara village.

———— *Angustifolia*, near the Minetaree village.

———— *Glabra*, alluvion of the Missouri, above the Big Bend.

Castilleja Sessiliflora, Upper Louisiana.

Myagrum Argenteum, on limestone rocks, Missouri.

Erysimum Lanceolatum, or, *Cheiranthus Erysimoides*, } a connecting link between Erysimum and Cheiranthus, used as medicine by the Aricaras.

Cleome Pinnata, on the prairies between the Aricaras and Mandans.

Cristaria Coccinea, on the bluffs of the Missouri, above the L'eau qui Court.

Hebiscus Militaris, ———— *Manihot*, } American Bottom, Illinois.

Ervum Multiflorum, opposite the Sepulchre bluffs, Missouri.

Viccia Stipulacca, Upper Louisiana.

Lathyrus Decaphyllus, sand alluvion of the Missouri, above the Big Bend.

Lupinus Pusillus, bluffs near Little Cedar Island.

Amorpha Fruticosa, common on the Missouri and Mississippi.

———— *Microphylla*, abundant near the Aricara village.

———— *Canescens*, on the prairie four miles west of St. Louis.

Astragalus Racemosus, ———— *Triphyllus*, ———— *Carnosus*, } on the bluffs opposite the mouth of Papillon Creek, and at the Aricara villages.

Dalea Aurea, on the prairies six miles below the L'eau qui Court.

———— *Laxiflora*, Aricara village.

Psoralea Cuspidata, on the bluffs near Chienne river.

———— *Longifolia,* near the Sepulchre bluffs. *Probably not a Psoralea,*

———— *Elliptica,* sand hills near the Big Bend.

———— *Esculenta,* bluffs near the mouth of Negro Fork, Merrimac river.

———— *Tenuiflora,* sand hills, Big Bend.

Cytisus Rhombifolius, at the mouth of Chienne river, and on arid places near the Aricara village.

Sonchus Pulchellus, banks of the Missouri, common.

Troximum Cuspidatum, common on the prairies between the Mahas and Mandans.

Eupatorium Altissimum, Missouri and Mississippi, common.

Oxytropis Lambertii, on the bluffs from the Maha village to the Poncars.

Artemisia Dracunculus,

———— *Cana,*

———— *Campestris,* } common on the Missouri.

———— *Santonica,*

Arnica fulgens, prairie from the Aricaras to the Mandans.

Cineraria Integrifolia, common on the Missouri.

Erigeron Hirsutum, Aricara village.

———— *Divaricatum,* common on the Missouri.

Senecio Pauperculus, prairie below the L'eau qui Court.

Aster Argenteus, prairie behind St. Louis, abundant.

Amellus Villosus, } common on the bluffs of the Missouri.

———— *Spinulosus,*

Galardia Acaulis, on the Missouri near the Aricara village. *Probably a Chaptalia.*

Rudbeckia Columnaris, bluffs above the Aricara village. *Most probably not a Rudbeckia, and ought to form a new genus.*

Iva Axillaris, about Chienne river.

Cheilanthes Dealbata and *Vestita,* Manitou rocks on the Missouri.

THE following letters on animalcula infusoria and the physiology of plants, although not apparently connected with this work, are yet of a nature so curious and interesting, that having obtained permission from the author (Mr. Bywater), I insert them. In the study of both those subjects we become acquainted with a great number of phenomena not to be explained upon any principles hitherto known. It is evident, therefore, that the right path has not yet been found. Mr. Bywater opens a fresh avenue : whether it will lead to the object, or terminate in a labyrinth, time and future discoveries may determine ; but having been present, along with others, when he has been engaged in his researches, and witnessed the results, I can state with confidence, that his conclusions, founded thereon, appeared to me far less improbable than what an explanation of the corals and coralines could have done to the most enlightened on those subjects one hundred years ago.

To Mr. BRADBURY.

Dear Sir,

Having mentioned to you the general character of a paper I had written for the Philosophical Journal, I was anxious it should have been published before you left this country, that I might have furnished you with a few copies, for the future consideration of you and your botanical friends in America; but am sorry to inform you that the editor received it too late for the whole to be published in the last Number : I have therefore availed myself of the opportunity offered by your protracted stay, to present you with an abstract of the whole document.

The first part of the communication chiefly relates to the different kinds of animalcules, and has appeared in the Philosophical Magazine; consequently I have made it as concise as I possibly could : but as the latter part of the paper contains some remarks on the principles of vegetation, I beg leave to call your particular attention to this part, as the view I have taken of the subject may lead to an investigation that will prove useful to your future botanical researches; and wishing you every success in your further travels, I remain,

Sir,

Your's most truly,

John Bywater.

Liverpool, May 27th, 1817.

OBSERVATIONS

ON THE

NATURE OF ANIMALCULES,

AND

PRINCIPLES OF VEGETABLE PHYSIOLOGY.

THAT many of the wonderful facts related of animalcules owe their strange and mysterious character to mistaken views respecting the real nature of these beings, is extremely evident, as they lead to conclusions at variance with themselves, and contrary to that simplicity and correctness of design we find displayed throughout every other part of the visible creation. The opinions which have been adopted, and the facts related of the hydra, or fresh water polypes, are so peculiarly wonderful, that even the writers of these well authenticated stories seem almost afraid they are passing the bounds of credibility by the relation. That these writers should have been astonished at the phenomena attending these beings, appears very natural, when we take into the account that they adopted the generally received opinion, and considered each polype as one distinct and complete animal. After the race of polypes was discovered, the attention of the curious was quickly called to the investigation of the subject, and they soon collected a great variety of facts, that seemed at variance with every well known principle in the animal economy.

Thus we are told on the best authority, that polypes exist after they have been turned inside out, like a turned glove, and that if one polype is thrust into the body of another, they form a union, and become one complete being. It is also asserted, that after they are cut into as many pieces as fancy can suggest, each part quickly becomes a perfect being, like the parent, or stock from which it was taken ; and that, when the heads of several are cut off, the heads and trunks may be brought indiscriminately into contact, and the head of one will become united to the trunk of another, and perform all the functions of the former head. Now these results, when considered agreeably to the generally received opinion, certainly appear mysterious, and contrary to every well established principle in the animal economy. Having investigated this branch of natural history, by making a great number of experiments and observations on the animalcula infusoria, I discovered the larger kind to be aggregate animalcules, or congeries of still smaller animals, living in lumps of mucilaginous matter,

derived in all probability from the decaying vegetables and their own secretions, to which they im-
parted, by an instinctive influence, an organization,
which enables them to move these mucilaginous
lumps by their aggregate force for all the purposes
of pleasure and existence. This principle of ag-
gregation, and their instinctive influence to orga-
nize their secretions, I have supposed to extend
through the whole race of animalcules, and that the
extraordinary phenomena attending polypes may
be accounted for by principles of this nature.

We know when a polype is cut into pieces, each
portion becomes a perfect being in a little time ;
this result is incompatible with the animal functions they evidently possess, if we consider them
as single and complete animals, and in all probability induced M. Buffon and others to adopt the
still more vague and improbable notion that animalcules are merely organic particles, and not living beings : but if we suppose polypes are aggregations or congeries of still smaller animals, we
may account for these wonderful phenomena in a
very easy manner, for when they are cut to pieces,
each part must contain some of these extremely
small animals, which will naturally produce, by
their instinctive energies, an aggregate animacule
like the parent stock, being the form best calculated
for their future purposes of existence. That the

whole tribe of the larger animalcules are congeries
of the smaller ones, will be rendered evident if
they are illuminated by an oblique light from the
sun, as they appear to be an assemblage of scintilating points, each posessing distinct powers of
motion. The results that led to the above conclusions were obtained during the late summer, but
in the succeeding autumn and winter, others were
obtained, that are equally favourable to this mode
of reasoning. About the latter end of September,
some water was procured from a stagnant pool, covered with a large quantity of green matter,
which appeared to be a species of conferva : this
I anticipated would furnish a great number of
interesting objects for the microscope. By examining a part of this water with the microscope,
it was found to be crowded with a vast number of
the enchelis, or small portions of green matter,
endowed with a degree of animation evidently derived from the small animals they contained, which
have generally been mistaken for intestines. These
aggregate animalcules appear rather more ellipti-
cal than an egg, and each end is nearly transparent, but generally the middle part seems the
abode of about twenty or more small animals, that
swing from side to side when these aggregations
are in motion, and are clearly the cause by which
they move from one place to another.

When the small animals increased in number, the middle of these mucilaginous masses, or what I have termed aggregate animalcules, swelled out till they became almost round, at the same time losing a great share of their activity. It was in this inactive state they united in large quantities, and floated without motion on the surface of the water; yet they remained in this apparently inanimate state but a short period, for this matter gradually lost its green vegetative appearance, and became a brown mucilaginous body, that assumed new characters. It was out of this mucilaginous matter that numerous aggregate animalcules, of various kinds, derived a more animated state of existence; but the gradual change of a large portion of it into different clusters of the polypes, termed vorticella, rendered this part of the process highly interesting, as it strongly supports the idea that all the larger kind of animalcula infusoria are congeries of small animals, living in organized portions of mucilaginous matter.

Nor is it an uninteresting fact, that during the winter, the green vegetative appearance, which seemed to reside in the mucilaginous part of what I have termed aggregate animalcules, varied with the weather. When it became mild, this greenness increased, but as quickly decreased when the weather became colder, giving strong indications

z

of the vegetable as well as animal nature of these little creatures.

This two-fold character is certainly curious; but it is manifested in a stronger manner by the production known among the natives of the East Indies by the name of " *Lalan lout,*" or sea grass; as its green appearance is such, that strangers mistake it for grass, yet when caught in the hand, it glides through the fingers, and withdraws itself into the sand, leaving an impression of its mucilaginous nature.

From these circumstances, it does not appear incompatible with the animal and vegetable processes to exist and go on together. May we not therefore conclude, with considerable probability, that they exist and proceed together throughout the whole vegetable process, as innumerable animalcules, similar to most I have mentioned, can be obtained from all young vegetable matter, when subject to infusion.

Among the class of sensitive plants, we have a peculiarly strong manifestation of a vital principle, and it is worthy of notice, that it is not that connected energy which runs through the whole frame, as in the animal economy, but appears to be distinct and contiguous portions of vitality, which are successively brought into action; for the contraction these plants display on being touched is not instantaneously communicated to every part, but seems to depend upon a succession of vital energies, which gradually run through the different parts of the vegetable. That the vitality of vegetables is somewhat like the vitality aggregate animalcules possess, is very probable; for some of them, like polypes, may be cut to pieces, and yet each piece will retain the power of forming or reproducing a complete vegetable. Having supposed that a vast number of extremely small animals live and extend their race with the vegetable growth, may we not also conceive it possible, that the beautiful forms and exquisite designs that obtain throughout the vegetable kingdom, originate from their directing influence. This opinion would certainly appear more satisfactory, if we could detect these small agents in the various parts of vegetables; but they are so extremely minute, that we can only just detect them, even under their aquatic character, when placed in the most favourable light for examination; therefore we cannot expect to detect them readily in vegetables, on account of their opacity.

Besides, the power of moving from one place to another, by which we detect aquatic animacules, is unnecessary to them, as they are in all probability fixed to their station like polypes in coralines,

and supplied with food by the vegetable organization they have instinctively established. I am well
aware that it will be difficult to conceive how such
a vast collection of extremely small animals can
act in concert, and direct by their influence the
extended organization of a vegetable; but in the
beautiful race of coralines, we have an ample display of this apparently very mysterious principle.
This class of organized bodies have such a close
resemblance to vegetables, that they were at one
period arranged by naturalists in the vegetable
kingdom; but now it is well known they are the
production or organization of an innumerable race
of small animals which inhabit them, and act in
concert for one general purpose. Although we
have the outward form of vegetables displayed
among this class of bodies, yet their internal organization bears little resemblance to the organic
structure of vegetables; but the reason for this
difference will appear evident when we consider
that coralines are placed in a fluid medium, which
supplies their numerous inhabitants with every necessary food. The water of the ocean, by its
constant motion, is continually passing and repass-
ing the receptacles in which these small animals
reside, and from which they can extend their
feelers to collect their food; therefore any peculiar
internal organization is not required to supply
them with nourishment; but the numerous class of
small beings we have supposed to inhabit and ex-

tend their race with the growth of vegetables, re-
ceive their supply of food chiefly from the roots:
hence the necessity of that curious organization
by which the vegetable process is carried forward, and they are supplied with the means of
subsistence.

But it is not in the race of coralines alone that
we find a collected body of small agents acting
in concert for a general purpose; for the beautifully branching vorticella, which, we obtain by vegetable infusion, are evidently the formation of a
congeries of small animals, which, in all probability, lived in the vegetables until they were li-
berated by the process of infusion. That vegetables are possessed of vitality, seems to be a fact
that scarcely admits a doubt, as the whole of the
vegetable phenomena point to a principle of this
nature; for who can view the spontaneous motion of various leaves, and the quick contraction
manifested by others, when simply touched with
any solid substance; the opening and shutting of
different flowers, at the approach of fine and foul
weather, while others open and shut at stated
periods, as well as numerous other phenomena
of a similar nature, without feeling a strong con-
viction that vitality is intimately connected with
the vegetable economy. These and many other
results that attend the vegetable process, will be
very imperfectly explained without the aid of such

a principle. Let us in imagination follow the vegetable changes that take place after a seed has been planted in the ground, until it shews a group of well blown flowers, and then endeavour to explain, by chemical and mechanical operations, how this additional matter attains those inimitable colours and that exquisite form and design it evidently does, and we shall almost be compelled to refer these changes to the directing energies of an instinctive intelligence. Let us also view the simple yet ingenious contrivances in many parts of flowers, for the purposes of fructification, and then try to explain their simple yet delicate mechanism by the undesigning energies of chemical affinities, and we shall discover how inadequate they are for the explanation of any such curious productions. Nor are these results better explained by referring them to a vitality which has been supposed common to the whole plant, as the facts I have mentioned show that the vitality of vegetables does not depend on any general or connected vitality that is common to the whole vegetable, but consists of distinct portions, and is of a similar nature to the vitality of aggregate animalcules: consequently, if we admit that vegetables are the receptacles in which myriads of small agents reside, these difficulties will be considerably removed; for to the influence of these agents we may fairly attribute the peculiar phe-

nomena of vegetation. If this analogical reasoning should prove conclusive, we shall find an extensive and promising field laid open for future
inquiry, which may ultimately lead to practical
deductions still more interestingly connected with
the sciences of botany and agriculture.

To Mr. BRADBURY.

Liverpool, July 16th, 1817.

DEAR SIR,

My communication to you on the principles of vegetable physiology contained some new
opinions, chiefly resting on the evidence of what
I considered strong analogies; but since that time,
several new results have been obtained, which
place these opinions on a more solid foundation.

Having seen it observed by different writers,
that the small capsules of the farina fecundas burst
when they come in contact with water, and throw
out a quantity of variously described matter, I was
induced to make some microscopical experiments,

under an impression they contained animalcules, or would exhibit strong marks of vitality, as they seem to be the consummation of the vegetable process.

In these experiments my expectations were not disappointed, as the farina of most flowers give out an abundance of animalcules, somewhat similar to the very small ones we obtain in such vast numbers by the process of infusion.

These results were obtained by putting a drop of water on a slip of glass, placed under the microscope, and then dropping a little farina into the water ; for in a few seconds, a violent internal motion commenced in the capsules, and they burst, emitting a quantity of glutinous looking matter, that manifested a high degree of animation, and presented some very curious objects for the microscope. In order to insure this beautiful variety, the sun must be bright, and the capsules so illuminated by an oblique light, as to give them a glittering appearance, and the water a dark blue colour.

When this is done, most of the farina, particularly that of the geraniums, will be seen to throw out silvery streams of beautifully animated matter. Sometimes this matter will issue in straight lines,

like streams of light, from which small portions
or animalcules will detach themselves, and float
about in various directions. From other capsules
these small animals are emitted almost on every
side, and render the water a sheet of scintilating
matter.

When this sparkling matter is highly magnified,
the animalcules appear like small opaque bodies,
writhing about, and in some cases floating down a
stream they create by the force with which they
quit the farina. One of these capsules becomes
a beautiful microscopic object, when the small animals issue with such force as to re-act upon the
capsule, and make it cross the field of view, as it
leaves behind an animated stream. These peculiar results will certainly afford an extensive field
for microscopical inquiries; but when connected
with the new views of vegetable physiology, perhaps they partake of a higher interest, as the circumstances attending these discoveries evidently
show, that small animals not only exist in, and extend their race with, vegetables, but in all probability are the real sources of vegetable life. That
these isolated collections of small beings are the
chief agents in forming, by their secretions and
instinctive influence, the embryo of a new plant,
does not appear improbable; for if an accumulation of them can construct such delicate vegetable

formation as the branching vorticella, when acting under their aquatic character, why may we not suppose them capable of instinctively constructing the embryo of a new vegetable, which is to be the abode of their future generations.

By the developement of one simple fact, we are often led directly, or by some imposing analogy, to the knowledge of many others. The discovery that the capsules of the farina contained numerous small animals, suggested the idea that similar agents might be detected in the other parts of vegetables, though probably without any apparent motion. This supposition was found consistent with experiment; for if the delicate leaves of flowers and vegetables are highly magnified and illuminated, numerous minute cylindrical opaque bodies, similar to those we obtain from the farina, are found embedded in almost every physical point of the leaves : a result which points out the probability that these small agents might be detected in the sap and juices of plants in a more active state.

The correctness of this inference is likewise readily established. If the juices of vegetables are pressed out, and examined upon a slip of glass, we may observe they abound with numerous small bodies, like those embedded in the leaves, which writhe about in a most animated manner;

thus proving by experiment what had been inferred only by analogy.

If, agreeably to this view of the subject, we contemplate the grandeur of an extensive forest, or even the more humble, yet not less pleasing variety of a beautifully enamelled meadow, and associate with this contemplation the idea that every leaf and flower is the habitation of myriads of sentient beings, we may perceive the end of that benevolence which seems to clothe the earth with herbs and flowers in such luxuriant profusion.

Nor is the benevolence of this vast design more conspicuous than its wisdom; for had these countless myriads of little beings floated in every direction through the atmosphere in search of food, their excessive numbers would have counteracted the enjoyments of almost every other part of the animal creation; but under their present character, they enjoy the light and air of heaven without giving the least annoyance, and are supplied with food by the general laws of matter, acting on a curious organization they have instinctively established.

Having detected these little agents in the farina, and found them embedded in almost every physical point of a vegetable; having also completely recognized their activity in the various juices of plants, it may be asked how far the different soils partake of this animating character, as the inquiry may lead to results intimately connected with the best interests of agriculture. To examine any soil agreeably to this view of the subject, it is necessary to place a little water on a slip of glass, or some transparent body, and drop a small portion of the soil into the water, and then we shall be enabled to observe what comparative quantity of these agents are given out by each soil, as they display sufficient activity to be discovered when the solution is stirred with any pointed body. From this assemblage of facts, we have the strongest evidence that the process of vegetation chiefly depends on the secretions and instinctive influence of this numerous class of agents. It may be difficult to conceive how they direct such an extensive process, yet it is equally difficult to comprehend the nature of that directing energy by which spiders form their various webs, or bees construct their curious hives :—it must be the unerring influence of Divinity which instinctively impels and guides these wonderful operations. Although I had often viewed the larger animalcula infusoria, and considered them as congeries of still smaller animals, yet I had no idea of the form and character of the little agents which compose these congeries, until I examined them by a similar light to that applied to the farina, and then it was evident that numerous small bodies, similar to those obtained from the juices of vegetables, were lodged in almost every point of these mucilaginous lumps, and were the source whence their power of motion was derived.

When paste eels, and the larger animalcula infusoria, are put into a little water, and the water so far evaporated as to impede their rapidity of motion, the individual energy of these little writhing bodies will appear extremely manifest, and impart to us a new idea respecting animal locomotion. The discovery of this new principle in the locomotive power of animals, in conjunction with several other peculiar results, connected with the animal economy, certainly involves questions of no trifling importance, which, if hastily pursued, might excite the fears of many, lest bold and inconsiderate speculators should carry the inquiry too far: but we have little to dread on this account; for the better we understand the nature and character of the secondary agents which the Deity employs to accomplish the vast designs of his stupendous providence, the greater must become our reverential admiration of his unbounded wisdom and benevolence. If M. Buffon and his speculative friends had ever attentively observed the playful activity some of the aggregate animal-

cules display, they must have concluded they
were living beings, and not merely organic particles, without life, moving by a species of internal
mechanism. That the whole race of polypes are
living beings we have very strong evidence; for
some of the vorticella induce a current to pass near
what is called their head, by the motion of small
fibrilæ, and devour the smaller animalcules which
are brought in contact with them by this current,
in a most voracious manner. The hydras also collect their food, and if they are fed with small red
worms, cut into bits, the red substance of the
worms may be seen dispersed through every part
of the hydra, which in a little time becomes
changed and assimilated to the general mass, except a small part, which is discharged, probably
on account of its not being fit for that purpose;
thus showing their powers of secretion, which are
energies generally considered as inseparable from
the principles of vitality.

Having shewn that aggregate animalcules possess secretive powers, and by a number of facts
proved they are congeries of small animals, similar
to those which abound in almost every part of a
vegetable, we are furnished with a tolerable solution to what are termed vegetable secretions, as in
all probability they are the supposed mysterious
agents by which these processes are carried for-

ward; and as we can discover that these little agents increase in number in the aggregate ani- malcules, we may perhaps, by a fair analogy, refer the hitherto unaccountable movement of the sap in plants to this multiplying principle. Although these little agents have generally a strong resem- blance to each other, yet those given out by the farina appear to differ in size when obtained from different flowers; therefore future discoveries, and a more minute inspection, may show that they vary in other respects, as well as in the general out- line of their dimensions, and that even themselves are composed of a congeries of still smaller beings. These agents are furnished by a variety of substan- ces; for a little black ink or milk put on a slip of glass, or a bit of raw sugar dropped into a little water, are objects worthy of inspection; nor will a scientific brewer find a small portion of wort, in a high state of fermentation, an uninteresting object, as it will be found completely animated, though none or very few of these agents are to be met with in fine ale, as the greater part of them make their escape with the barm.

Sometime ago, I mentioned to you it was proba- ble that the beautiful plumage of the feathered tribe owed its design and variety to an agency of this kind, as the various phenomena attending the growth of feathers bear such a strong analogy to many of the vegetable phenomena: since then I have found, by inspection, that these little opaque bodies are inclosed in almost every part of a feather.

These and numerous other results open a wide field for investigation; but several circumstances have induced me to wave the inquiry for the present: nevertheless, should you meet with any new and interesting facts in America, I shall be glad if you will send me a detail, agreeably to your promise, the first opportunity; and believe me,

Your's truly,

JOHN BYWATER.

In the preceding letters on animalcula infusoria, Mr. Bywater has placed that subject in a perfectly new point of view; and although I add a few remarks, I must acknowledge that it is with much diffidence. The inferences, as respects the nature and organization of vegetables, are fit only for the discussion of those infinitely my superiors in talent. Respecting the animalcula infusoria, it certainly appears to me, that by admitting the correctness of his reasoning on that subject, a great many of those doubts and perplexities, which have hitherto continued to exist, notwithstanding the many acute

researches that have been made, will entirely va-
nish. It has always been observed, that the mode
by which other animals were propagated never
applied to the production of animalcula infusoria; but the principles laid down by Mr. Bywater remove this difficulty. The singular property
of the polypes, and that after subdivision a new
organization should take place, is not more surprising, if we admit his opinion to be correct, than
that a swarm of bees should make honey-combs
similar to those they left in the hive. The extreme
tenuity to which the animated creation is carried,
is perhaps not less difficult to be conceived by the
human mind than the magnitude of the sun. It
can therefore make nothing against the opinion of
Mr. Bywater, if it implies the agency of animals
inconceivably minute.

That animated bodies should be invariably produced in water wherein vegetable matter has been
infused, and kept at a proper temperature, has long
been known; but by what means, or how they
derived their existence, has never been clearly
pointed out. Spallanzani proved beyond a doubt,
that the agency of the atmosphere was not necessary to their production, and that vegetable matter,
infused in boiling water, and confined in a glass
vessel, hermetically sealed, soon produced a vast
number of animated bodies. That they had a pre-

existent state in the body of the vegetable, seems by much the most rational way of accounting for their appearance; and it follows from the observations and experiments of Mr. Bywater, that myriads of living animalculæ do exist in the juices of plants. The question is then, for what use or purpose are they intended? This question Mr. Bywater answers, by assigning to them the most important part in the scale of creation,—that of being the agents of vegetable organization. This opinion is partly founded on reasoning analogically, which affords some very strong arguments in his favour. Whoever is the least acquainted with animal economy, knows that, besides the eternal law which compels animals individually to perform certain acts in a certain manner *only*, there is another by which thousands, and even millions, are compelled to act as if governed by one mind and one intelligence; and whether these acts are performed by individuals, or an association of myriads, the organs given to them are calculated in the best possible manner to produce the intended effect, and that effect is the best possible to promote the ends and purposes of their existence. The formation of corals and coralines, the operations of bees, ants, and the termites, are sufficient instances to illustrate this principle.

In the physiology of vegetation, innumerable

facts tend to prove a species of vitality in plants
not to be explained upon any principles yet laid
down, nor can it depend on chemical or mechanical combination, or the operation of external
agencies. The flowers of the three species of *alli-*
onia found on the Missouri, open within a few minutes of sun-setting, and perish at the time of its
rising, and this whether the evening or morning is
cloudy or not. When rye is in blossom, a few an-
thers only are protruded in each head : cut these
off on a warm day, and in a few minutes more will
be protruded from other florets, and the experiment
may be repeated with equal success several times.
There is a description of vitality, manifesting itself
in the disposition of certain parts of some plants to
take a kind of repose, which is called the sleep of
plants. This vitality will remain even after those
parts have been separated from the plant to which
they were attached. Flowers accustomed to go to
sleep at certain periods, retain that faculty after
they are placed in a flower pot. The leaf of a vine,
cut from the branch, and hung up by a thread, will
turn to the light of itself. Facts of this kind are
so numerous, that a review of them would fill a vo-
lume. I shall therefore close these remarks, by
noticing the most singular fact yet known as relates
to the physiology of plants, copied from Sir James
Edward Smith's Introduction to Physiological and
Systematic Botany. " But of all flowers, that of

the barberry bush is most worthy the attention of
a curious physiologist. In this the six stamens,
spreading moderately, are sheltered under the con-
cave tips of the petals, till some extraneous body,
as the feet or trunk of an insect in search of honey,
touches the inner part of each filament near the
bottom. The irritability of that part is such, that
the filament immediately contracts there, and consequently strikes its anther, full of pollen, against
the stigma. Any other part of the filament may
be touched without this effect, provided no con-
cussion be given to the whole. After a while the
filament retires gradually, and may again be stimu-
lated ; and when each petal, with its annexed filament, is fallen to the ground, the latter, on being
touched, shews as much sensibility as ever." This
fact proves that in one single plant thousands of
distinct vitalities may exist.

F I N I S.

SMITH and GALWAY, Printers,
Liverpool.

ERRATA.

Page 15, line 10, for *Arundinacea macrocarpon* read *Arundinaria ma-
crosperma.*

17,   12, after *the* insert *petrified.*

21,   7, for *Equicetum* read *Equisetum.*

44, note,   for *Columbo migratorius* read *Columba migratoria.*

62, line 26, for *calve* read *calves.*

67,   22, for *We-ken* read *Wa-ken.*

91,   15, for *Rhus glabra* read *Rhus glabrum.*

98,   21, for *if was* read *if it was.*

99,   17, for *corlieu* read *curlew.*

118, note,   for *by French* read *by the French.*

258, line   6, for *Gleditsia* read *Gleditschia.*

288,   26, for *Gleditsia* read *Gleditschia.*